Discovering Geometry

WITH THE GEOMETER'S SKETCHPAD®

KEY CURRICULUM PRESS
Innovators in Mathematics Education

Project Team

Contributing Editors	Masha Albrecht, Dan Bennett, Sarah Block
Production Manager	Luis Shein
Production Coordinator	Susan Parini
Editorial Assistant	Romy Snyder
Cover Design	Dennis Teutschel

Publisher

Steven Rasmussen

Editorial Director

John Bergez

Discovering Geometry with The Geometer's Sketchpad® Disks

Key Curriculum Press guarantees that the disks that accompany this book are free of defects in materials and workmanship. A defective disk will be replaced free of charge if returned within 90 days of the purchase date. After 90 days, there is a $10.00 replacement fee.

Limited Reproduction Permission

Key Curriculum Press
P.O. Box 2304
Berkeley, CA 94702
(510) 548-2304
editorial@keypress.com
http://www.keypress.com

Printed in the United States of America.
ISBN 1-55953-209-2

10 9 8 7 6 5 4 3   00 99 98 97

Contents

This book contains replacement lessons for *Discovering Geometry*, second edition, whenever the use of The Geometer's Sketchpad® can enhance the lesson. If dynamic geometry is not a particularly useful tool for a lesson, this book does not contain a replacement lesson. For example, you will notice that there are no replacement lessons here that correspond to Chapter 1 from *Discovering Geometry*.

Also, Chapter 0, the first chapter in *Discovering Geometry*, is at the end of this book, because the constructions required to create the art in this chapter would be difficult as beginning Sketchpad™ lessons.

Introduction		vii
Common Commands and Shortcuts		x
Activities		
Chapter 2	**Introducing Geometry**	1
2.6	Defining Triangles	5
2.7	Special Quadrilaterals	7
Chapter 3	**Using Tools of Geometry**	9
3.2	Constructing Perpendicular Bisectors	10
3.3	Constructing Perpendiculars	12
3.4	Constructing Angle Bisectors	13
3.7	Constructing Points of Concurrency	14
3.8	The Centroid	17
Chapter 4	**Line and Angle Properties**	19
4.1	Discovering Angle Relationships	20
4.2	Discovering Properties of Parallel Lines	21
4.3	Midpoint and Slope Conjectures	23
4.4	Slopes of Parallel and Perpendicular Lines	26
4.5	Equations of Lines	28
Chapter 5	**Triangle Properties**	31
5.1	Triangle Sum Conjecture	32
5.2	Discovering Properties of Isosceles Triangles	33
5.3	Triangle Inequalities	35
5.4	SSS, SAS, and SSA Congruence Shortcuts?	37
5.5	ASA, SAA, and AAA Congruence Shortcuts?	40
5.7	Isosceles Triangles Revisited	42
Chapter 6	**Polygon Properties**	43
6.1	Polygon Sum Conjecture	44
6.2	Exterior Angles of a Polygon	46
6.3	Discovering Kite and Trapezoid Properties	48
6.4	Discovering Properties of Midsegments	50
6.5	Discovering Properties of Parallelograms	52
6.6	Discovering Properties of Special Parallelograms	53

Chapter 7	**Circles**	**55**
7.1	Defining Circles	56
7.2	Discovering Chord Properties	59
7.3	Discovering Tangent Properties	61
7.4	Arcs and Angles	62
7.5	The Circumference/Diameter Ratio	64

Chapter 8	**Transformations and Tessellations**	**65**
8.1	Transformations	66
8.2	Properties of Isometries	69
8.3	Symmetry	72
8.6	Tessellations Using Only Translations	74
8.7	Tessellations That Use Rotations	76

Chapter 9	**Area**	**77**
9.1	Areas of Rectangles and Parallelograms	78
9.2	Areas of Triangles, Trapezoids, and Kites	80
9.4	Areas of Regular Polygons	82
9.5	Areas of Circles	83

Chapter 10	**Pythagorean Theorem**	**85**
10.1	The Theorem of Pythagoras	86
10.2	Is the Converse True?	88
10.4	Two Special Right Triangles	89
10.5	Multiples of Right Triangles	91
10.7	Distance in Coordinate Geometry	92

Chapter 12	**Similarity**	**93**
12.2	Similarity	94
12.3	Similar Triangles	95
12.4	Indirect Measurement with Similar Triangles	97
12.5	Corresponding Parts of Similar Triangles	99
12.6	Proportion with Area and Volume	102
12.7	Proportional Segments by Parallel Lines	104

Chapter 13	**Trigonometry**	**107**
13.1	Trigonometric Ratios	108
13.3	The Law of Sines	110

Chapters 15 and 16	**Deductive Reasoning**	**111**
Project	Non-Euclidean Geometries	112
16.7	Midsegment Conjectures	114

Chapter 0	**Geometric Art**	**117**
0.2	Line Designs	118
0.3	Daisy Designs	120
0.4	Op Art	121
0.7	Islamic Art	123
0.8	Perspective	125

Lesson Guides

Introduction to The Geometer's Sketchpad   **128**

Chapter 2	**Introducing Geometry**	
2.6	Defining Triangles	129
2.7	Special Quadrilaterals	130

Chapter 3	**Using Tools of Geometry**	
3.2	Constructing Perpendicular Bisectors	131
3.3	Constructing Perpendiculars	132
3.4	Constructing Angle Bisectors	133
3.7	Constructing Points of Concurrency	134
3.8	The Centroid	136

Chapter 4	**Line and Angle Properties**	
4.1	Discovering Angle Relationships	138
4.2	Discovering Properties of Parallel Lines	139
4.3	Midpoint and Slope Conjectures	141
4.4	Slopes of Parallel and Perpendicular Lines	143
4.5	Equations of Lines	144

Chapter 5	**Triangle Properties**	
5.1	Triangle Sum Conjecture	145
5.2	Discovering Properties of Isosceles Triangles	146
5.3	Triangle Inequalities	147
5.4	SSS, SAS, and SSA Congruence Shortcuts?	148
5.5	ASA, SAA, and AAA Congruence Shortcuts?	149
5.7	Isosceles Triangles Revisited	150

Chapter 6	**Polygon Properties**	
6.1	Polygon Sum Conjecture	151
6.2	Exterior Angles of a Polygon	152
6.3	Discovering Kite and Trapezoid Properties	153
6.4	Discovering Properties of Midsegments	155
6.5	Discovering Properties of Parallelograms	156
6.6	Discovering Properties of Special Parallelograms	157

Chapter 7	**Circles**	
7.1	Defining Circles	159
7.2	Discovering Chord Properties	161
7.3	Discovering Tangent Properties	162
7.4	Arcs and Angles	163
7.5	The Circumference/Diameter Ratio	164

Chapter 8	**Transformations and Tessellations**	
8.1	Transformations	165
8.2	Properties of Isometries	166
8.3	Symmetry	168
8.6	Tessellations Using Only Translations	169
8.7	Tessellations That Use Rotations	170

Chapter 9	**Area**	
9.1	Areas of Rectangles and Parallelograms	171
9.2	Areas of Triangles, Trapezoids, and Kites	172
9.4	Areas of Regular Polygons	174
9.5	Areas of Circles	175
Chapter 10	**Pythagorean Theorem**	
10.1	The Theorem of Pythagoras	176
10.2	Is the Converse True?	177
10.4	Two Special Right Triangles	178
10.5	Multiples of Right Triangles	179
10.7	Distance in Coordinate Geometry	180
Chapter 12	**Similarity**	
12.2	Similarity	181
12.3	Similar Triangles	182
12.4	Indirect Measurement with Similar Triangles	184
12.5	Corresponding Parts of Similar Triangles	186
12.6	Proportion with Area and Volume	187
12.7	Proportional Segments by Parallel Lines	188
Chapter 13	**Trigonometry**	
13.1	Trigonometric Ratios	189
13.3	The Law of Sines	190
Chapters 15 and 16 Deductive Reasoning		
Project	Non-Euclidean Geometries	191
16.7	Midsegment Conjectures	192
Chapter 0	**Geometric Art**	
0.2	Line Designs	194
0.3	Daisy Designs	195
0.4	Op Art	196
0.7	Islamic Art	197
0.8	Perspective	198

Introduction

Discovering Geometry has attracted innovative teachers since its first edition was published in 1989. Many of those first users were also enthusiastic about burgeoning educational technology—particularly Logo and the Geometric Supposers—that was so well suited to a discovery approach. Now Key Curriculum Press offers what we think is the most powerful integrated package of curriculum and technology available: the second edition of *Discovering Geometry* and The Geometer's Sketchpad, Key's widely successful ground-breaking software for doing geometry dynamically. *Discovering Geometry with The Geometer's Sketchpad* is intended to make this integration seamless.

Please note that The Geometer's Sketchpad software does *not* come with this book. The disks accompanying this book contain only sketches and scripts. To use these files, you must first install The Geometer's Sketchpad on your computer. The Geometer's Sketchpad full-featured program is separately available from Key Curriculum Press. A demonstration version of The Geometer's Sketchpad comes with the *Discovering Geometry Teacher's Resource Book.* You may use that version to review these sketches and scripts. However, the only authorized classroom use of the demonstration version is with the demonstrations that accompany the *Teacher's Resource Book.* See the following page for more about the disks that accompany *Discovering Geometry with The Geometer's Sketchpad.*

What's in This Book

This book is a collection of Geometer's Sketchpad activities that mirror *select* lessons in *Discovering Geometry*—activities in this book have the same titles and lesson numbers as the corresponding *Discovering Geometry* lessons. You'll see in the table of contents that these activities don't appear with consecutive lesson numbers—some lessons appear to be missing. We chose lessons that seem well suited to computer explorations on the basis of our experiences and on those of Sketchpad users and *Discovering Geometry* field testers. There may be other lessons in *Discovering Geometry* that you think would make good Sketchpad activities. And you may prefer to do many of this book's activities in the way described in the text, without using a computer. In fact, if you did all the activities in this book, you'd probably be overdoing it with Sketchpad at the expense of giving students experience with other tools of investigation. This book is not intended to replace *Discovering Geometry.* Instead it's intended to give you enough options to have maximum flexibility.

Using This Book

To use this book, you should be familiar with The Geometer's Sketchpad. Most students can pick up the basics of the software pretty quickly, but it helps, to start anyway, if you're one step ahead of students, knowing what they can do with the software and anticipating difficulties they might encounter. You can introduce yourself to virtually all the features of the software by doing all the Guided Tours in the first part of the *User Guide and Reference Manual,* which comes with Sketchpad.

The activities in this book don't demand the use of all of Sketchpad's many features. Students should find most, if not all, of the directions they need to use the software in the activities themselves. The first activities in this book, Introduction to The Geometer's Sketchpad and The Geometer's Sketchpad Checklist, give students a chance to discover much of the logic of the program for themselves. You can also reproduce the list of common commands found at the end of this introduction and give it to students to refer to while they're learning the program.

While doing geometric art is a great way to start the school year, we don't recommend you start with the Chapter 0 activities in this book as students' introduction to Sketchpad. An important reason for starting *Discovering Geometry* with art is so that students can become familiar with using a compass and a straightedge. Also, the art activities in this book will be easier for students to do after they have some

Sketchpad experience. That's why Chapter 0 comes at the end of this book. You certainly don't need to save the art activities for last. Let your students try them whenever you think it's appropriate.

Each activity in this book has a teacher comments page, which includes a section titled Lesson Guide/*Discovering Geometry* Correlation, where you'll find suggestions for how to use the activity. For the most part, the activities are designed to be covered in one class period and to cover the same material as their corresponding lessons in *Discovering Geometry*. So you could, in theory, use many of these Sketchpad activities in place of the *Discovering Geometry* lessons without adding any instructional time. However, as you know, presenting a *Discovering Geometry* lesson involves more than setting students loose on investigations. You typically spend time at the beginning of class introducing the subject and at the end of class bringing closure to it and working examples. That time, especially the end-of-class closure, is more difficult to find in a computer lab, where the investigations are likely to take most of the period. Students may get through the investigations but may not be prepared for the exercise set without some in-class practice. So be prepared to spend an extra day on a lesson that you do with Sketchpad. Later in the year, as students get more proficient with Sketchpad and more persistent with problem solving, you might need that extra day less often.

When you choose an activity to do with your students, try it out yourself first so you can prepare how you want to introduce the activity, can decide whether to divide tasks, can anticipate questions, and can get a sense of how long it might take. Read the teacher comments and be sure that if any pre-made sketches or scripts are required they'll be available. Decide whether this as an activity you want all your students to do in the computer lab, or a group of students to do as an extension, or to do yourself as a demonstration on an overhead display.

The Sketches and Scripts on Disk

In most of the activities, students start with a blank sketch and perform a construction themselves that they then investigate. So most of the sketches on the disk that accompanies this book are just examples of what students would construct in the course of doing the activity. They're not to be used with the activity. You can think of them as answers. In the teacher comment pages, these sketches are listed under the heading Example Sketches.

A few activities require students to start out with a pre-made sketch or script. In these activities, the required sketches or scripts are listed under the heading Required Sketches and Scripts.

Finally, a number of activities can be streamlined by having students use script tools. Many Pythagorean theorem activities, for example, require students to construct squares. Rather than going through the construction each time they need a square, students can set a script tool folder that contains a script for a square. You'll find three folders of scripts on the disk: regular polygons, triangle special points, and Poincaré geometry tools. To set a script tool folder, choose Preferences in the Display menu and click More. In the Advanced Preferences dialog, under Set Script Tool Folder, click Set. (You may have to click Clear first.) Navigate in the pop-up menu to find the desired folder. Click the Set button. Click Continue, then click OK to dismiss the Preferences dialog.

The following activities require either pre-made sketches or scripts.

Lesson 2.6: Defining Triangles
- Classify Triangles (Mac) or ch02\classtri.gsp (Windows)
- Altitude/Median (Mac) or ch02\altmed.gsp (Windows)

Lesson 2.7: Special Quadrilaterals
- Trapezoid & Kite (Mac) or ch02\trapkite.gsp (Windows)
- Special Quads (Mac) or ch02\spquads.gsp (Windows)

Lesson 3.8: The Centroid

Note: Students make these scripts in Lesson 3.7. They are required for Lesson 3.8.

- Centroid (Mac script) or ch03\trnglpts\centroid.gss (Windows script)
- Incenter (Mac script) or ch03\incenter.gss (Windows script)
- Circumcenter (Mac script) or ch03\crcmcntr.gss (Windows script)
- Orthocenter (Mac script) or ch03\orthcntr.gss (Windows script)

Lesson 4.3: Midpoint and Slope Conjectures

- Slope of a Line (Mac) or ch04\slopelin.gsp (Windows)

Lesson 5.4 : SSS, SAS, and SSA Congruence Shortcuts?

- SSS (Mac) or ch05\sss.gsp (Windows)
- SAS (Mac) or ch05\sas.gsp (Windows)
- SSA (Mac) or ch05\ssa.gsp (Windows)

Lesson 5.5 : ASA, SAA, and AAA Congruence Shortcuts?

- ASA (Mac) or ch05\asa.gsp (Windows)
- AAA (Mac) or ch05\aaa.gsp (Windows)

Lesson 6.3: Discovering Kite and Trapezoid Properties

- Quad Family (Mac) or ch06\quadfmly.gsp (Windows)

Lesson 6.4: Discovering Properties of Midsegments

- Quad Family (Mac) or ch06\quadfmly.gsp (Windows)

Lesson 6.6: Discovering Properties of Special Parallelograms

- Quad Family (Mac) or ch06\quadfmly.gsp (Windows)

Lesson 9.4: Areas of Regular Polygons

- 5/Pentagon (By Edge) (Mac) or repoly\4byedge.gss (Windows)

Lesson 9.5: Areas of Circles

- To a Circle (Mac) or ch09\polycirc.gsp (Windows)

Lesson 10.2: Is the Converse True?

- Triple Check (Mac) or ch10\triplchk.gsp (Windows)

Lesson 10.5: Multiples of Right Triangles

- Triple Check (Mac) or ch10\triplchk.gsp (Windows)

Lesson 10.7: Distance in Coordinate Geometry

- Coordinate Distance (Mac) or ch10\distance.gsp (Windows)

Lesson 12.3: Similar Triangles

- AAA Similarity? (Mac) or ch12\AAA_sim.gsp (Windows)
- SSS Similarity? (Mac) or ch12\SSS_sim.gsp (Windows)
- SSA Similarity? (Mac) or ch12\SSA_sim.gsp (Windows)
- SAS Similarity? (Mac) or ch12\SAS_sim.gsp (Windows)

Project: Non-Euclidean Geometries

Poincaré Disk Starter (Mac sketch) or Poincar\Poincare.gsp (Windows sketch)

all scripts in the Poincaré folder (Mac) or Poincar directory (Windows)

Common Commands and Shortcuts

These are some commands used all the time in Sketchpad but that can be hard to remember how to do. To be enabled, some commands require you to select certain objects in your sketch. The required selections are usually quite logical. To construct a perpendicular line, for example, you need to select a straight object for your new line to be perpendicular to and a point for your new line to pass through. Once you get the hang of the logic behind the commands, they'll all be easier to remember.

To open a new sketch

Choose New Sketch in the File menu.

To close a sketch

Choose Close in the File menu or click in the close box in the upper left corner of the sketch.

To undo or redo

Choose Undo in the Edit menu or type Command-z (Mac) or Control-z (Windows). You can undo as many steps as you want, all the way back to the state your sketch was in when last saved. To redo, type Command-r (Mac) or Control-r (Windows).

To deselect everything

Click in any blank area of your sketch with the Selection Arrow tool. Do this before you make selections required for a command so that you can be sure you don't have anything extra selected when you choose that command.

To show or hide a label

Position the finger of the Text tool over the *object* and click. The hand will turn black when it's correctly positioned to show or hide a label. Point labels are capital letters, starting with *A*. Straight object labels are lowercase letters, starting with *j*.

To change a label

Position the finger of the Text tool over the *label* and double-click. The letter "A" will appear in the hand when it's positioned over a label.

To change line weight, color, or shade

Select the object whose appearance you want to change and choose the appropriate submenu in the Display menu. To shade an area you must first construct and select a polygon interior (see below).

To select an angle

Select three points, making the angle vertex your middle selection. Three points are the required selections to **construct an angle bisector** (Construct menu), to **measure an angle** (Measure menu), or to **mark an angle of rotation** (Transform menu).

To construct a polygon interior

Select the vertices (points) of the polygon in consecutive order around the polygon. Then choose Polygon Interior from the Construct menu.

To mark a center of rotation or dilation

Use the Selection Arrow tool to double-click on the point. A brief animation indicates that you've marked it.

To use the calculator

Double-click on any measure in a sketch. Once the calculator is active, you can move it by dragging its title bar. To enter a measure into the calculator, click in your sketch on the measure. Once you've created the expression you want to calculate, click OK.

To set a script tool folder

Choose Preferences in the Display menu and click More. In the Advanced Preferences dialog, under Set Script Tool Folder, click Set. (You may have to click Clear first.) Navigate in the pop-up menu to find the desired folder. Click the Set button. Click Continue, then click OK to dismiss the Preferences dialog.

Using the Student Worksheet

It is a good idea to have students write down their responses to the questions in Sketchpad lessons. The worksheet on the following page is generic enough to work for almost any of the lessons in this book. You can make many copies of these and have them on hand all the time. You may want each student to turn in a completed worksheet for a lesson, you might have group members collect and check each worksheet, or you could have students file these worksheets as part of their notes. In order to save paper you could have students share copies of the lesson itself as well as copies of the worksheets. As always, try to make sure students share the role of recorder, reader, and mouse user.

Your name _____

Your group members' names _____

Worksheet for a Geometer's Sketchpad Lesson

Lesson name _____   Lesson number _____

Investigate

Use the lines below to record your answers to questions from the Investigate section. Make sure to number your answers. If your answers include new conjectures, remember to add the conjectures to the list of conjectures in your notebook. If you run out of room here, use the back of the page.

_____

_____

_____

_____

_____

_____

_____

_____

Explore More

Record your answers to any Explore More questions below.

_____

_____

_____

Activities

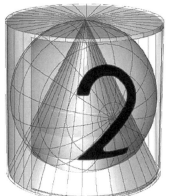

Introducing Geometry

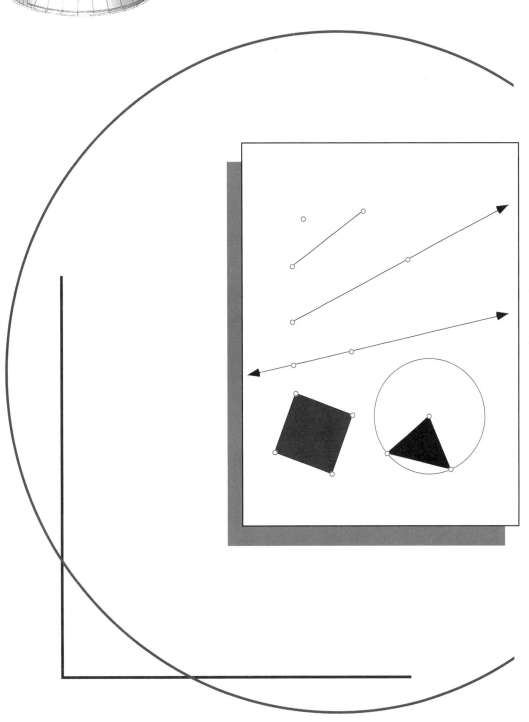

Introduction to The Geometer's Sketchpad

Students have found that they can figure out a great deal about using The Geometer's Sketchpad without a lot of directions. For the first part of this lesson, your instructions are simply to play with this new geometric tool. Spend at least 15 minutes exploring with The Geometer's Sketchpad and keep track of how many different things you figure out how to do by listing them on this page. Make sure to share the mouse with your group members or partner.

_____

_____

_____

_____

_____

_____

_____

_____

_____

_____

_____

_____

_____

_____

_____

_____

_____

_____

_____

_____

_____

_____

_____

_____

_____

_____

_____

_____

_____

_____

_____

_____

The Geometer's Sketchpad Checklist

Now that you have had a chance to explore on your own with Sketchpad, you can start keeping track of your expertise using this checklist. Your teacher may give you time to share and exchange your checklist skills with other groups. You also may have time later on in the year to update this list to keep track of your new skills.

Check off what you can do as you learn. These tasks are in no particular order and some of them you may not learn until later on in the year! If you have no idea how to start on a task, skip it and go on to the next one. Your goal is *not* to check off all the skills; just check off as many as you can.

(0-20 checked) novice

(20-40 checked) apprentice

(40-60 checked) expert

_____ 1. Construct a triangle. Make sure that it stays a triangle as you drag different parts of it around on the screen.

_____ 2. Select everything using the Select All command.

_____ 3. Select segments and points using the Selection Arrow tool.

_____ 4. Deselect an individual object, keeping the others selected.

_____ 5. Drag with the Selection Arrow tool to select only a few objects in the same part of the screen.

_____ 6. Move a single object to a different part of the screen.

_____ 7. Draw a circle.

_____ 8. Draw a line.

_____ 9. Draw a ray.

_____ 10. Label a point. Also hide its label.

_____ 11. Label circles, lines and segments.

_____ 12. Move and change the label on an object.

_____ 13. Delete an object.

_____ 14. Hide an object.

_____ 15. Create an angle and measure it.

_____ 16. Make a pair of Hide/Show buttons.

_____ 17. Construct a Golden Rectangle. Make sure it stays a Golden Rectangle as you drag different parts of it around the screen.

_____ 18. Use the Text tool to display your name.

_____ 19. Draw a line and find its slope.

_____ 20. Calculate the radius of a circle after measuring its circumference.

_____ 21. Change the text style of a caption.

_____ 22. Measure the three angles of a triangle and use Sketchpad's calculator to find their sum.

_____ 23. Construct an angle and then create the bisector of that angle.

_____ 24. Construct a line perpendicular to another line through a point not on the line.

_____ 25. Construct a line parallel to another line through a point not on the line.

_____ 26. Tessellate your screen with regular hexagons. Make sure the tessellation stays intact no matter how you drag or distort it.

____27. Construct a circle. Then construct a circle that is always tangent to the first circle.

____28. Make a script tool that constructs the centroid of a triangle.

____29. Create a script with a recursive step that builds stages of a fractal.

____30. Measure the length of a segment.

____31. Animate a point around a circle.

____32. Construct an animated car that rolls down a road.

____33. Construct a square, and make sure it is always a square no matter which parts of it you drag around.

____34. Construct an equilateral triangle, and make sure it is always equilateral no matter which parts of it you drag around.

____35. Create a table of values.

____36. Add entries to the table using the keyboard, the mouse and the Measure menu.

____37. Change the length of a segment.

____38. Close a document.

____39. Size a window so that you can see two windows at the same time.

____40. Find the midpoints of the sides of a triangle.

____41. Create a script that draws a triangle and finds its midpoints.

____42. Replay a script using the Given at the beginning of the script.

____43. Mark a center of rotation or dilation.

____44. Dilate a triangle using the Dilate command.

____45. Reflect an object across a line.

____46. Construct a point that traces a parabola.

____47. Make a script tool that constructs a square.

____48. Trace the locus of a point.

____49. Animate a trace.

____50. Turn on the x-y grid.

____51. Graph the linear function $y = 2x+3$.

____52. Find the equation of a line.

____53. Construct the interior of a circle and shade it dark blue.

____54. Draw a polygon and construct its interior.

____55. Find the area of the interior of a polygon.

____56. Find the perimeter of a polygon.

____57. Rotate an object 39° counterclockwise.

____58. Rotate an object 95° clockwise.

____59. Translate an object by a specified vector.

____60. Record a sound and create an action button to play the sound. Record appropriate sounds only!

Lesson 2.6

Defining Triangles

In this lesson, you'll experiment with an ordinary triangle and with special triangles that were constructed with constraints. The constraints limit what you can change in the triangle when you drag so that certain relationships among angles and sides always hold. By observing these relationships, you will classify the triangles.

Investigation 2.6

Sketch A: Classifying Triangles

Step 1   Open the sketch Classify Triangles (Mac) or ch02\classtri.gsp (Windows).

Step 2   Drag different vertices of each of the four triangles to observe and compare how the triangles are constrained.

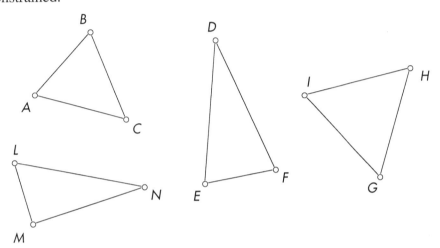

Investigate

1.   Which of the triangles seems the least constrained (the easiest to change by dragging)? Explain.

2.   Which of the triangles seems the most constrained (the hardest to change by dragging)? Explain.

3.   To classify the triangles by their angles, you need to recall the definitions of acute, obtuse, and right angles. Measure the three angles in △ABC. (To measure an angle, hold down Shift and select three points, with the vertex your middle selection.) Determine whether each angle is acute or obtuse. Now drag a vertex of your triangle. How many acute angles can a triangle have?

4.   How many obtuse angles can a triangle have?

5.   △ABC can be either an obtuse triangle or an acute triangle. One other triangle in the sketch can also be either acute or obtuse. Which triangle is it?

6.   Which triangle is constrained to be a right triangle, no matter what you drag?

7.   Which triangle is always an equiangular triangle, no matter what you drag?

8.   *Scalene, isosceles,* and *equilateral* are terms used to classify triangles by relationships among their sides. Measure the lengths of the three sides of △ABC. If none of the side lengths are equal, the triangle is a scalene triangle. If two or more of the sides are equal in length, the triangle is isosceles. If all three sides are equal in length, it is equilateral. Because △ABC has no constraints, it can be any type of triangle. But which type of triangle is △ABC most of the time?

9.   Name a triangle besides △ABC that is scalene most of the time.

10. Which triangle (or triangles) is (are) always isosceles, no matter what you drag?

11. Which triangle is always equilateral, no matter what you drag?

In questions 12–16, state whether the triangle described is possible or not possible. To check whether each is possible, try manipulating the triangles in the sketch to make one that fits the description. If it's possible to make the triangle, sketch an example on your paper.

12. An obtuse isosceles triangle

13. An acute right triangle

14. An obtuse equiangular triangle

15. An isosceles right triangle

16. An acute scalene triangle

17. Write definitions of *acute triangle, obtuse triangle, right triangle, scalene triangle, isosceles triangle,* and *equilateral triangle.*

Sketch B: Medians and Altitudes in Triangles

Step 1   Open the sketch Altitude/Median (Mac) or ch2\altmed.gsp (Windows). Δ*ABC* has no special constraints.

Step 2   Drag points *A, B,* and *C* and observe how segments *BE* and *BD* behave.

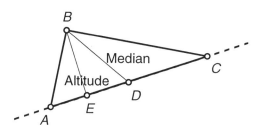

Investigate

18. Segment *BD* is a **median**. What do you think is the definition of *median of a triangle*? Make measurements to test or confirm your guess.

19. Segment *BE* is an **altitude**. When does $\overline{BE}$ fall outside the triangle? When does it fall inside the triangle?

20. Define *altitude of a triangle.*

21. How many medians does a triangle have? How many altitudes?

Explore More

1.   See if you can construct a triangle like Δ*LMN* in Investigation 2.6A that stays a right triangle no matter what you drag. For hints, go back to the sketch and choose Show All Hidden in the Display menu. Use the Information tool (the question mark) and click on parts of the construction to see how they are related.

2.   In a new sketch, see if you can construct an isosceles triangle that always stays isosceles, or an equilateral triangle that is always equilateral. For hints, go back to the sketch Classify Triangles and show all hidden.

3.   In a new sketch, see if you can construct a triangle with an altitude that stays an altitude no matter how you drag the triangle. Once you've figured out how to do it, construct the other two altitudes, too. Is it possible for exactly one altitude to fall outside the triangle? Exactly two? All three? Explain.

©1997 Key Curriculum Press

Lesson 2.7

Special Quadrilaterals

Trapezoids, kites, parallelograms, rectangles, rhombuses, and squares have special properties that distinguish them from other quadrilaterals. In this investigation, you'll experiment with these shapes to discover what makes them different from "ordinary" quadrilaterals and from one another.

Investigation 2.7

Sketch A: Trapezoids and Kites

Step 1   Open the sketch Trapezoid & Kite (Mac) or trapkite.gsp (Windows).

Step 2   Drag various parts of these quadrilaterals. Each quadrilateral has a different set of constraints in its construction that keeps it what it is.

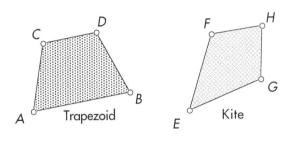

Step 3   Measure the slopes of the four sides of the trapezoid.

Investigate

1. If lines (or segments) have the same slope, they are parallel. How many pairs of sides in the trapezoid are parallel?

2. If you're very careful, it's possible to drag vertices so that both pairs of opposite sides in the trapezoid are parallel, or at least close to it. However, in that case, the figure is no longer a trapezoid. Given that restriction, define *trapezoid*.

3. Measure the lengths of the four sides of the kite. Which sides are equal in length?

4. If you're very careful, it's possible to drag vertices so that all four sides in the kite are equal in length, or at least close to it. In that case, the figure is no longer a kite. Given that restriction, define *kite*.

Sketch B: Parallelograms

Step 1   Open the sketch Special Quads (Mac) or 4quads\spquads.gsp (Windows).

Step 2   Drag various parts of these quadrilaterals.

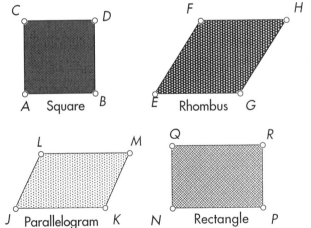

Investigate

Each quadrilateral has a different set of constraints in its construction that keeps it what it is. For example, no matter what part you drag, the square stays a square. You can drag vertices of the rhombus to make different shapes, but you'll still have a rhombus.

5. Measure the slopes of the sides of the parallelogram. Drag parts of the figure. How many pairs of sides are parallel? Define *parallelogram*.

6. Measure the angles in the rectangle. Drag parts of the figure. Define *rectangle*.

7. Measure the side lengths in the rhombus. Drag parts of the figure. Define *rhombus*.

8. Measure the side lengths and angles of the square. Define *square*.

9. Drag the rhombus so that it's also a rectangle (or at least close to it). What's the best name for this shape?

10. Drag the rectangle so that it's also a rhombus (or at least close to it). What's the best name for this shape?

11. Based on your observations in questions 9 and 10, write a definition of *square* different from your definition in question 8.

In questions 12–16, copy the sentence, choosing *always, sometimes,* or *never* to make the sentence true.

12. A parallelogram is (always/sometimes/never) a square.

13. A rectangle is (always/sometimes/never) a rhombus.

14. A square is (always/sometimes/never) a rhombus.

15. A rectangle is (always/sometimes/never) a parallelogram.

16. A parallelogram that is not a rectangle is (always/sometimes/never) a square.

Explore More

1. See if you can come up with methods for constructing trapezoids and kites that always stay trapezoids and kites. Describe your methods.

2. Open a new sketch and see if you can come up with ways to construct special parallelograms. Describe your methods.

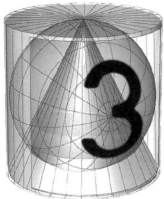

Using Tools
of Geometry

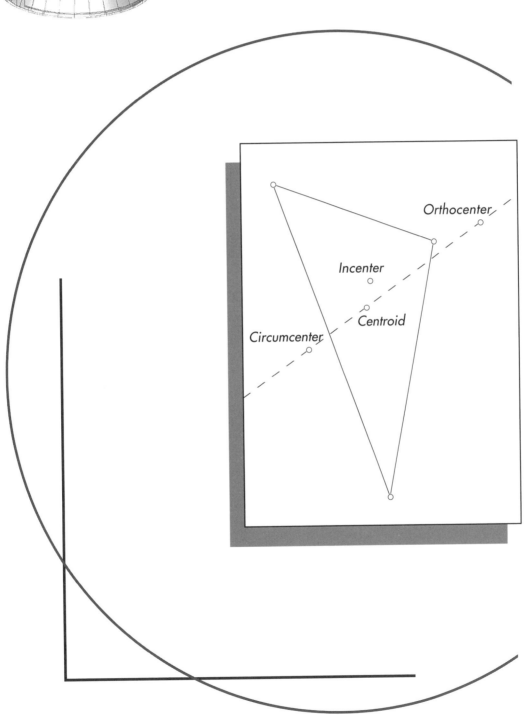

Lesson 3.2

Constructing Perpendicular Bisectors

The perpendicular bisector of a segment is a line that divides the line segment into two congruent parts (bisects it) and that is also perpendicular to the line segment. In this activity, you'll construct a perpendicular bisector using only Sketchpad's freehand tools. As you do so, you'll investigate properties of perpendicular bisectors.

Investigation 3.2.1: The Perpendicular Bisector Conjecture

Sketch

Step 1   Construct $\overline{AB}$.

Step 2   Construct a circle starting at center point A and releasing the mouse with the cursor positioned at point B. Point B should control the circle's radius.

Step 3   Construct a circle from center point B to radius control point A.

Step 4   Construct $\overleftrightarrow{CD}$, where C and D are the points of intersection of the circles.

Step 5   Construct point E, the point of intersection of $\overline{AB}$ and $\overleftrightarrow{CD}$.

Step 6   Construct point F anywhere on $\overleftrightarrow{CD}$.

Step 7   Hide the circles.

Step 8   Select points A and F and choose Distance in the Measure menu. Also measure BF.

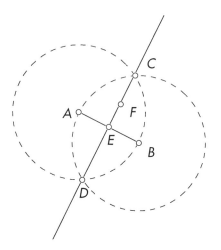

Investigate

1.   Line CD is the perpendicular bisector of $\overline{AB}$. Move points A and B. What's special about point E?

2.   Move point F up and down the line. What can you say about any point on a segment's perpendicular bisector? Write a conjecture (C-1: Perpendicular Bisector Conjecture).

Investigation 3.2.2: The Converse

Next you'll investigate the Converse of the Perpendicular Bisector Conjecture.

Sketch

Step 1   Continue in the same sketch and construct a free point G, not on any object.

Step 2   Measure the distances from G to points A and B.

GA = 1.29 cm
GB = 2.24 cm

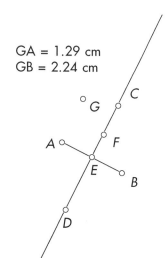

Investigate

3.   If a point is not on the perpendicular bisector of a segment, is it equally distant from the segment's endpoints?

4.   Drag point G until it is equally distant (or as close to equally distant as you can get) from points A and B. Find several locations for point G such that $GA = GB$. What do you notice about every such location? Write the Converse of the Perpendicular Bisector Conjecture (C-2).

Explore More

1. Open a new sketch. Draw a segment and come up with a shortcut for constructing a perpendicular bisector using the Construct menu. Describe how you did it.

2. Draw a line AB and a point C not on the line. Double-click the line to mark it as a mirror for reflection. Select point C and choose Reflect in the Transform menu. Construct segment CC'. Drag different parts of your sketch. How are $\overleftrightarrow{AB}$ and $\overline{CC'}$ related?

Lesson 3.3

Constructing Perpendiculars

Measuring the distance between two points is easy, but how do you measure the distance between a point and a line? There are lots of different distances, depending on what point you measure to on the line. What's the shortest distance? That's what you'll investigate in this activity.

Investigation 3.3.2: Shortest Distance Conjecture

Sketch

Step 1   Construct $\overleftrightarrow{AB}$.

Step 2   Construct $\overline{CD}$, where point C is not on $\overleftrightarrow{AB}$ and point D is on $\overleftrightarrow{AB}$.

Step 3   Select point C and $\overleftrightarrow{AB}$ and choose Distance in the Measure menu.

Step 4   Measure CD.

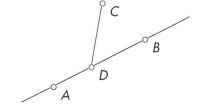

Investigate

1.   Which is greater, CD or the distance from point C to $\overleftrightarrow{AB}$?

2.   When you ask Sketchpad to measure the distance from a point to a line, it measures the shortest distance. To discover what that shortest distance is, drag point D until the distance CD is as small as you can make it. It should be approximately equal to the distance from C to $\overleftrightarrow{AB}$. Select point C and $\overleftrightarrow{AB}$ and choose Perpendicular Line in the Construct menu. What can you say about the shortest distance from a point to a line? Write your response as a conjecture (C-3: Shortest Distance Conjecture).

Explore More

Model this problem on Sketchpad:

There's a sewage treatment plant at the point where two rivers meet. You want to build a house near the two rivers (upstream, naturally, from the sewage plant), but you want the house to be at least 5 miles from the sewage plant. You visit each of the rivers to go fishing about the same number of times, but, being lazy, you want to minimize the amount of walking you do. (You want the sum of the distances from your house to the two rivers to be minimal.) Where should you build your house?

A model of the rivers and plant is shown below. Add constructions to this model to investigate possible locations for the house.

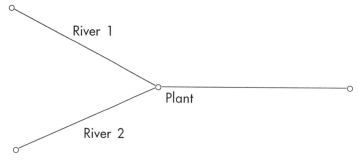

Lesson 3.4

Constructing Angle Bisectors

An angle bisector is a ray that has its endpoint at the vertex of the angle and that divides the angle into two angles of equal measure. In this investigation, you'll investigate a special property of points on an angle bisector.

Investigation 3.4.1: The Angle Bisector Conjecture

Sketch

Step 1   Use the Ray tool to draw $\overrightarrow{AB}$ and $\overrightarrow{AC}$.

Step 2   Select, in order, points *B*, *A*, and *C* and choose Angle Bisector in the Construct menu.

Step 3   Construct point *D* on the angle bisector.

Step 4   Select point *D* and $\overrightarrow{AB}$ and choose Distance in the Measure menu.

Step 5   Measure the distance from point *D* to $\overrightarrow{AC}$.

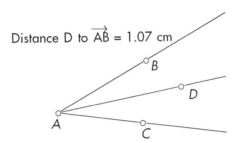

Distance D to $\overrightarrow{AB}$ = 1.07 cm

Investigate

1.   To confirm that $\overrightarrow{AD}$ bisects ∠*BAC*, measure angles *BAD* and *DAC*. (To measure an angle, select three points, with the vertex in the middle.) Drag point *A*, *B*, or *C* to change ∠*BAC*. How do the angle measures compare?

2.   Drag point *D* and observe the distances from point *D* to the two sides of the angle. Write a conjecture about any point on the bisector of an angle (C-4: Angle Bisector Conjecture).

Explore More

1.   In a new sketch, draw rays *AB* and *AC*. Double-click on $\overrightarrow{AC}$ to mark it as a reflection mirror. Select $\overrightarrow{AB}$ and choose Reflect in the Transform menu. Drag different points in your sketch. How are $\overrightarrow{AB}$ and $\overrightarrow{AC}$ related?

2.   Write the Converse of the Angle Bisector Conjecture. Is the converse true? Explain how to demonstrate this with Sketchpad.

3.   See if you can construct an angle bisector using only Sketchpad's freehand tools—not the Construct menu.

Lesson 3.7

Constructing Points of Concurrency

In these three investigations, you'll discover some properties of angle bisectors, perpendicular bisectors, and altitudes in a triangle.

Investigation: Angle Bisectors in a Triangle

Sketch

Step 1   Construct triangle *ABC*.

Step 2   Select points *B, A,* and *C* and choose Angle Bisector in the Construct menu to bisect ∠*A*.

Step 3   Construct the bisector of ∠*B*.

Step 4   Construct point *D* where these two rays intersect.

Investigate

1.   Construct the bisector of ∠*C*. What do you notice about this third angle bisector? Drag the vertices of the triangle to see if this is always true.

2.   If you were blindfolded and drew three lines on a piece of paper, do you think they would intersect in a single point? When lines that lie in the same plane *do* intersect in a single point, they're said to be **concurrent**. Using the word *concurrent*, write a conjecture about the three angle bisectors of a triangle (C-6).

3.   The point of concurrency of the angle bisectors in a triangle is called the **incenter**. Select point *D* and $\overline{AB}$ and choose Distance in the Measure menu. Measure the distances from point *D* to the other two sides. Drag parts of the triangle; then write a conjecture about the incenter of a triangle (C-10).

Sketch (Angle Bisectors Continued)

Step 5   Continuing in the same sketch, hide the rays.

Step 6   Use the Text tool to double-click on the label *D*. Change it to *I* for incenter.

Step 7   Select the entire figure, but not the measures. Choose Make Script in the Work menu.

Step 8   Save the script in the folder indicated by your teacher and name the script Incenter. You'll need this script for Explore More and for Lesson 3.8.

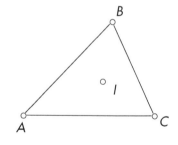

Investigation: Perpendicular Bisectors in a Triangle

Sketch

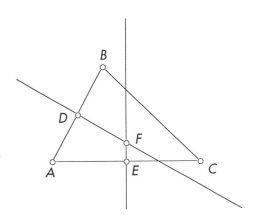

Step 1   Open a new sketch.

Step 2   Construct $\triangle ABC$ and drag it so that it appears to be acute.

Step 3   Construct points D and E, the midpoints of $\overline{AB}$ and $\overline{AC}$.

Step 4   To construct the perpendicular bisector of $\overline{AB}$, select point D and $\overline{AB}$ and choose Perpendicular Line in the Construct menu.

Step 5   Construct the perpendicular bisector of $\overline{AC}$.

Step 6   Construct point F where these two perpendicular bisectors intersect.

Investigate

4.   Construct the perpendicular bisector of $\overline{BC}$. Drag any vertex of $\triangle ABC$. Write a conjecture about the three perpendicular bisectors of a triangle (C-7). Include in your conjecture any differences you observe between acute and obtuse triangles.

5.   The point of concurrency of the perpendicular bisectors of a triangle is called the **circumcenter**. Measure distances from the circumcenter to each of the three vertices of the triangle. Drag parts of the triangle; then write a conjecture about the circumcenter of a triangle (C-9).

Sketch (Perpendicular Bisectors Continued)

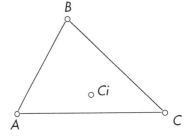

Step 7   Continuing in the same sketch, hide the lines and midpoints.

Step 8   Change the label of point F to Ci for circumcenter.

Step 9   Select the entire figure except for the measures. Choose Make Script in the Work menu.

Step 10   Save the script in the folder indicated by your teacher and name the script Crcmcntr. You'll need this script for Explore More and for Lesson 3.8.

Investigation: Altitudes in a Triangle

Sketch

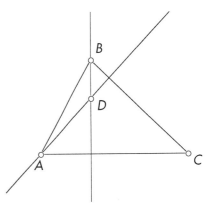

Step 1   Open a new sketch.

Step 2   Construct $\triangle ABC$ and drag it so that it appears acute.

Step 3   Select $\overline{AC}$ and point B and choose Perpendicular Line in the Construct menu. This line contains an altitude of $\triangle ABC$.

Step 4   Construct another line through point A that contains an altitude.

Step 5   Construct point D, the point of intersection of these two lines.

Investigate

6. Construct the line containing the third altitude in △*ABC*, through point *C*. Drag any vertex of △*ABC*. Write a conjecture about the three altitudes (or the lines through the altitudes) of a triangle (C-8). This point of concurrency is called the **orthocenter**. Include in your conjecture what you observe about the orthocenter in acute and obtuse triangles.

Sketch (Altitudes Continued)

Step 6   Continuing in the same sketch, hide the lines.

Step 7   Change the label of point *D* to *O* for orthocenter.

Step 8   Select the entire figure. Choose Make Script in the Work menu.

Step 9   Save the script in the folder indicated by your teacher and name the script Orthcntr. You'll need this script for Lesson 3.8.

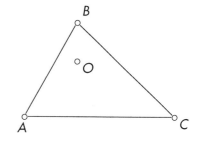

Explore More

1. Open a new sketch and play your script Crcmcntr. Draw a circle centered at the circumcenter and drag to one of the three vertices of the triangle. A circle that passes through each vertex of a polygon is a **circumscribed circle**. Explain why a circumscribed circle is centered at the circumcenter of a triangle.

2. Open a new sketch and play your script Incenter. Draw a circle centered at the incenter and drag it out until it just touches the three sides of the triangle. A circle that touches each side of a polygon at exactly one point is an **inscribed circle**. Explain why a circle inscribed in a triangle is centered at the incenter. See if you can construct an inscribed circle that stays inscribed no matter how you drag the triangle.

Lesson 3.8

The Centroid

In Lesson 3.7, you discovered that the three angle bisectors in a triangle are concurrent, as are the three perpendicular bisectors and the three altitudes. Would you be surprised to discover that the three medians in a triangle are concurrent?

Investigation 3.8.1

Sketch

Step 1   Construct triangle *ABC*.

Step 2   Construct the midpoint *D* of $\overline{AC}$ and construct median *BD*.

Step 3   Construct the midpoint *E* of $\overline{AB}$ and construct median *CE*.

Step 4   Construct point *F* where these medians intersect.

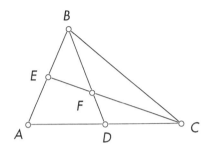

Investigate

1.   Construct the third median, from point *A* to $\overline{BC}$. Drag any vertex of △*ABC*. Write a conjecture about the three medians of a triangle (C-11).

Investigation 3.8.2

Sketch

Step 5   Continuing in the same sketch, use the Text tool to double-click on the label *F*. Change this label to *Ce* for centroid.

Step 6   Measure the distance from *B* to *Ce* and the distance from *Ce* to *D*.

Step 7   Drag vertices of △*ABC* and look for a relationship between *BCe* and *CeD*.

Step 8   Select the two measures and choose Tabulate in the Measure menu.

Step 9   Change the triangle and double-click on the table values to add another entry.

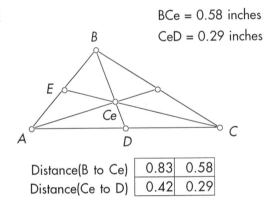

BCe = 0.58 inches
CeD = 0.29 inches

| Distance(B to Ce) | 0.83 | 0.58 |
| Distance(Ce to D) | 0.42 | 0.29 |

Investigate

2.   Keep changing the triangle and adding entries to your table until you can see a relationship between the distances *BCe* and *CeD* and are convinced that this relationship holds for any triangle. Write a conjecture (C-12).

3.   Select the table and choose Plot Table Data in the Graph menu. In the Plot Points dialog, click Plot. (You don't want to change any of the data.) You should get a graph with several collinear points. Explain the significance of the slope of this line.

Investigation 3.8.3

In this investigation, you'll look for a relationship among four points of concurrency: the incenter, the circumcenter, the orthocenter, and the centroid. You'll need the scripts for the incenter, circumcenter, and orthocenter that you made in Lesson 3.7. But first you'll need to continue in your centroid sketch to make a centroid script.

Sketch

Step 10 Continuing in the same sketch, hide the midpoints and medians of $\triangle ABC$, but don't hide the centroid.

Step 11 Select the entire triangle, including the centroid, but don't select any measures or any part of the graph. Choose Make Script in the Work menu. Name the script Centroid and save it in a folder or directory indicated by your teacher.

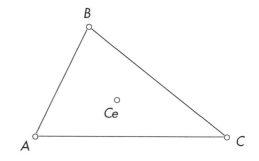

In steps 12–21, you'll learn how to use this centroid script and the scripts you made for other points of concurrency as script tools. If you make scripts of complicated constructions, script tools make it very easy to repeat those constructions any time you want.

Step 12 Open a new sketch.

Step 13 Choose Preferences in the Display menu and click More.

Step 14 In the More Preferences dialog, under Set Script Tool Folder, click Set. (You may have to click Clear first.)

Step 15 Find the folder where you saved your points of concurrency scripts and open it. You should have scripts for the centroid, circumcenter, incenter, and orthocenter.

Step 16 Click the Set button.

Step 17 Click Continue; then click OK to dismiss the Preferences dialogs.

Step 18 You should now have a tool at the bottom of your toolbox that looks like a double arrowhead. Press on this tool and choose Centroid.

Step 19 Click and drag three times to construct a triangle and its centroid.

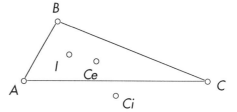

Step 20 Press the Script tool and choose Incenter. Use this tool to construct the incenter on the same triangle you made in step 19.

Step 21 Choose Crcmcntr in the Script tool and use it to construct the circumcenter in the same triangle.

Investigate

4. The three points of concurrency you've constructed in this triangle so far all have special properties that you discovered earlier. The orthocenter is feeling left out. Choose Orthcntr in the Script tool and use it to construct the orthocenter in the triangle with the other three points of concurrency. Three of these four points are collinear. Drag the triangle to see which three these are. The line they lie on is called the **Euler line**. Which of the three points lie on the Euler line? Write a conjecture (C-13).

5. When all four points are collinear, what kind of triangle do you have?

6. When all four points are coincident (the same point), what kind of triangle do you have?

7. Make your triangle scalene; then construct a segment connecting two of the three points on the Euler line and passing through the third. This is the **Euler segment**. What are its endpoints? What is the point on the Euler segment?

8. The point on the Euler segment divides it into two parts. Measure the distances between the endpoints of each of these two parts. Look for a relationship between these distances and write a conjecture (C-14).

Lesson 4.1

Discovering Angle Relationships

When two lines intersect, they form four angles whose vertices are the point of intersection. In this activity, you'll investigate relationships between pairs of these angles.

Investigation 4.1

Sketch

Step 1   Construct $\overleftrightarrow{AB}$ and $\overleftrightarrow{AC}$. Drag point A to make sure it is a control point of both lines.

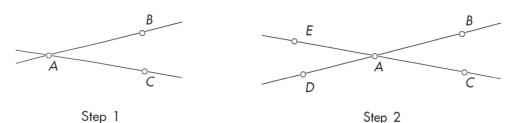

Step 1   Step 2

Step 2   Construct point D on $\overleftrightarrow{AB}$ so that A is between D and B. Also construct E on $\overleftrightarrow{AC}$ so that A is between E and C.

Step 3   Measure the four angles: $\angle BAC$, $\angle CAD$, $\angle DAE$, and $\angle EAB$.
Remember that to measure an angle in Sketchpad you need to select three points on the angle, using the vertex as the middle point.

Investigate

1. Drag points B and C. Record anything you notice about the relationships among the angles.

2. In your sketch, $\angle BAC$ and $\angle DAE$ are a pair of **vertical angles**. This name is related to the fact that the angles share the same vertex. $\angle CAD$ and $\angle EAB$ are another pair of vertical angles. Make a conjecture about the measures of vertical angles (C-15).

3. In your sketch, $\angle BAC$ and $\angle CAD$ are a **linear pair.** This name comes from the fact that the outside sides of the angles form a line.

    a. Find all the other linear pairs in your sketch.

    b. Write a conjecture about the relationship between angles in a linear pair (C-16). Use Calculate in the Measure menu to test your conjecture.

4. Describe any situations you find where the angles in a linear pair are equal.

Explore More

1. Two intersecting lines form four angles. If you knew the measure of one of the angles, you could find the measures of the other three using your new conjectures. Now suppose you have three lines intersecting in a single point to form six angles.

    a. How many angle measures would you need to know in order to find the other angle measures?

    b. Describe any situations where all the angles are congruent.

2. Suppose you have four lines intersecting in a single point to form eight angles. Answer parts a and b from Explore More 1 above for this different case.

3. Now generalize your results from the last two questions. Suppose you had n lines intersecting to form $2n$ angles. Answer parts a and b from Explore More 1 above for this general case.

Line and Angle Properties

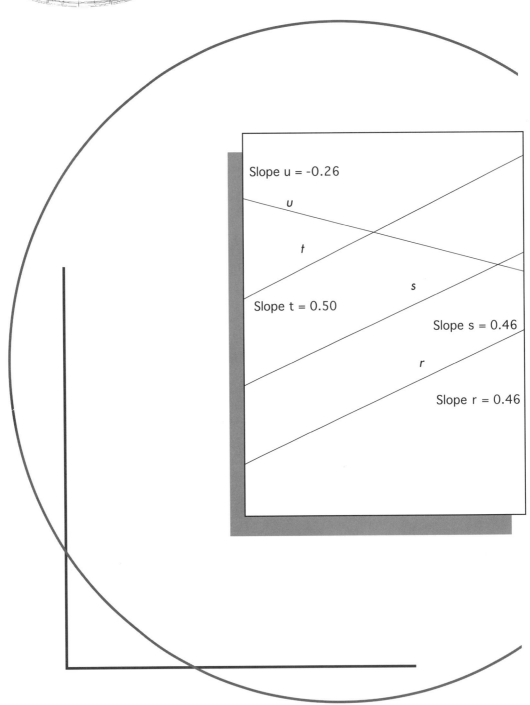

Lesson 4.2

Discovering Properties of Parallel Lines

In this investigation, you'll discover relationships among the angles formed when you intersect parallel lines with a third line called a **transversal**.

Investigation 4.2.1

Sketch

Step 1   Construct $\overleftrightarrow{AB}$ and point C, not on $\overleftrightarrow{AB}$.

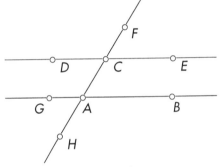

Step 1   Steps 2 and 3

Step 2   Construct a line parallel to $\overleftrightarrow{AB}$ through point C.

Step 3   Construct $\overleftrightarrow{CA}$. Drag points C and A to make sure you attached the three lines correctly.

Step 4   Construct points D, E, F, G, and H as shown on the right.

Step 5   Measure the eight angles in your figure. Remember that to measure angles in Sketchpad you need to select three points on the angle, making sure the middle point is always the vertex.

Step 4

Investigate

1.   When two parallel lines are cut by a transversal, the pairs of angles formed have specific names and properties. Drag point A or B and watch which angles stay congruent. Also drag the transversal $\overleftrightarrow{CA}$. Describe how many of the eight angles you measured appear to be always congruent.

2. $\angle FCE$ and $\angle CAB$ are an example of a pair of **corresponding angles.**

   a. List all the pairs of corresponding angles in your construction.

   b. Write a conjecture that describes what you observe about corresponding angles (C-17a: CA Conjecture).

3. $\angle ECA$ and $\angle CAG$ are an example of a pair of **alternate interior** angles.

   a. List all the pairs of alternate interior angles in your construction.

   b. Write a conjecture that describes what you observe about alternate interior angles (C-17b: AIA Conjecture).

4. $\angle FCE$ and $\angle HAG$ are an example of a pair of **alternate exterior** angles.

   a. List all the pairs of alternate exterior angles in your construction.

   b. Write a conjecture that describes what you observe about alternate exterior angles (C-17c: AEA Conjecture).

5. Combine the three conjectures you made in questions 2–4 into a single conjecture about parallel lines that are cut by a transversal, and call it the Parallel Lines Conjecture (C-17).

6. Suppose, in a similar sketch, all you knew was that the angle pairs described above had the properties you observed. Would you be sure that the original pair of lines were parallel? Try to answer this question first without using the computer.

Investigation 4.2.2: The Converse

Sketch

Now you can investigate the Converse of the Parallel Lines Conjecture on the computer.

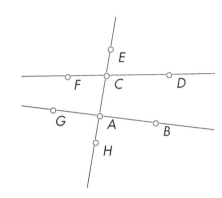

Step 1   Draw two lines that are not quite parallel. Intersect both lines with a transversal.

Step 2   Measure all eight angles formed by the three lines. Add points if you need them.

Step 3   Move the lines until the pairs of angles match the conjectures that you made in the Investigate section above.

Investigate

7. Lines with equal slopes are parallel. To check to see if your lines are parallel, measure their slopes. Write a new conjecture to summarize your conclusions (C-18: Converse of the Parallel Lines Conjecture).

Explore More

1. ∠ECA and ∠BAC in the third figure at the beginning of this activity are sometimes called **consecutive interior** angles. In a new sketch, find all pairs of consecutive interior angles and make a conjecture describing their relationship.

2. ∠FCD and ∠HAG in the third figure at the beginning of this activity are sometimes called **consecutive exterior** angles. Find pairs of consecutive exterior angles and make a conjecture describing their relationship.

3. You can use the Converse of the Parallel Lines Conjecture to construct parallel lines. Construct a pair of intersecting lines $\overrightarrow{AB}$ and $\overleftrightarrow{AC}$ as shown. Select, in order, points C, A , and B, and choose Mark Angle in the Transform menu. Double-click point C to mark it as a center for rotation. You figure out the rest. Explain why this works.

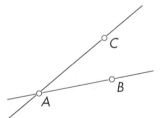

Lesson 4.3

Midpoint and Slope Conjectures

In this activity, you will discover a method for finding the midpoint of a line segment using the coordinate grid. You will also find a method for finding the slope of a line. You may have learned about calculating slope in a previous class.

Investigation 4.3.1: The Midpoint Conjecture

Sketch

Step 1   In a new sketch, use the Graph menu to choose Show Grid. Also use the Graph menu to make sure that Snap to Grid is checked.

Step 2   Draw segment CD anywhere on your grid.

Step 3   Construct the midpoint of $\overline{CD}$. Change the label of this point to *Midpoint*.

Step 4   Use the Measure menu to find the coordinates of all three points on $\overline{CD}$.

Step 5   Line up the three measures vertically so it is easier for you to compare the numbers.

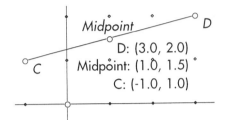

Midpoint   D
D: (3.0, 2.0)
C   Midpoint: (1.0, 1.5)
C: (-1.0, 1.0)

Investigate

1.   To look for patterns, drag the endpoints of your segment and watch the six coordinate measurements carefully. It might be easier to focus on the *x*-coordinates first, then pay attention to the *y*-coordinates later. The pattern is also easier to see when the segment is shorter and in the first quadrant. Keep experimenting until you are sure you have found a pattern that describes the relationship between the coordinates of the endpoints of a segment and the coordinates of the segment's midpoint. Record your observations.

2.   Now you can generalize by writing a conjecture using variables. Suppose that one endpoint of a segment has the coordinates (x_1, y_1) and the other has the coordinates (x_2, y_2). Record the coordinates of the midpoint and write your results as a conjecture (C-19: Coordinate Midpoint Conjecture).

3.   In the Graph menu, turn off Snap to Grid. Now drag your segment into a new position. Test your conjecture from question 2 using the coordinates of the new endpoints. Record your results.

Investigation 4.3.2: The Slope of a Line

If you are a skier, you might describe the slope of a hill on which you skied. If you are a carpenter, you might describe the slope of a roof you built. An economist might describe the slope of a graph. In this activity, you'll first experiment with the slopes of various lines. Then you will play a game, with a partner, that challenges you to recognize various slopes. Finally, you will make a conjecture about how to calculate the slope of a line.

Sketch A

Step 1   In a new sketch, choose Show Grid from the Graph menu. Use the Graph menu to turn off Snap to Grid.

Step 2   Draw any line. Measure its slope using the Measure menu.

Step 3   Select one of the points on the line and drag this point to rotate the line. Observe the effect on its slope.

Step 4   Select the line itself and drag it around. Observe the effect on its slope.

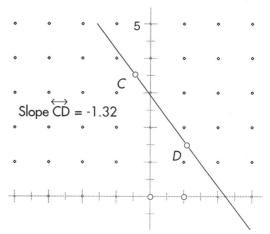

Investigate

Answer the following questions to prepare yourself for the Slope Game.

4.   Which lines have a positive slope, and which have a negative slope?

5.   What is the slope of a horizontal line?

6.   How can you tell a steeper slope from a shallower slope?

7.   What is the slope of a vertical line?

Sketch B: Playing the Slope Game

Play this game with a partner.

Step 1   Draw five different random lines in your sketch. Make sure no labels are showing.

Step 2   Select all five lines and measure their slopes.

Step 3   Challenge your partner to match each measured slope with a line. Your partner is allowed to touch only measurements, to move them next to the lines they match. The lines and the points are "off limits" until all the measurements have been matched up with lines.

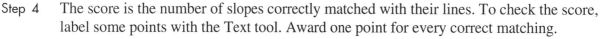

Step 4   The score is the number of slopes correctly matched with their lines. To check the score, label some points with the Text tool. Award one point for every correct matching.

Step 5   Switch roles, remove labels, scramble the lines, and play the game again. Add more lines to make the game more challenging.

Investigate

8.   Record your total scores after at least one complete round of the Slope Game.

Sketch C: Calculating the Slope of a Line

Step 1 Open up the sketch Slope of a Line (Mac) or ch04\slopelin.gsp (Windows). Make sure you understand all the measurements showing in the sketch.

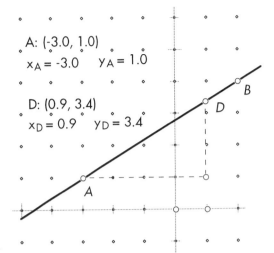

A: (-3.0, 1.0)

$x_A = -3.0$ $y_A = 1.0$

D: (0.9, 3.4)

$x_D = 0.9$ $y_D = 3.4$

Step 2 Calculate the vertical change, or change in y between point D and point A, using only the calculator and the measurements already showing in your sketch. Do not make any new measurements. This change is often called the "rise."

Step 3 Calculate the horizontal change, or change in x between point D and point A, using only the calculator and the measurements already showing in your sketch. This change is often called the "run."

Step 4 Use the calculator to divide the rise by the run.

Investigate

9. Drag point D and observe your ratio *rise/run*. Record your observations.

10. Drag point A and point B until the line is horizontal. Describe the ratio *rise/run* for a horizontal line.

11. Drag point A and point B until the line is vertical. Describe the ratio *rise/run* for a vertical line.

12. Describe the line when the ratio *rise/run* is negative.

13. Finally, measure the slope of your line and make a conjecture about how to calculate the slope of a line using coordinates.

14. Now you can generalize your conjecture using other variables. Suppose that one point on the line has the coordinates (x_1, y_1) and another has the coordinates (x_2, y_2). Find the slope of the line using these four variables and write your answers as part of a conjecture (C-20: Slope of a Line Conjecture).

Explore More

1. Construct a segment and measure the coordinates of its endpoints.

   a. Use the calculator to calculate the coordinates of the midpoint. (Hint: To find a single x- or y-coordinate from a coordinate pair, select the coordinate pair and look in the Values menu in the calculator.) Then select, in order, the calculation of the x-coordinate and the calculation of the y-coordinate and choose Plot as (x, y) in the Graph menu. Drag an endpoint and report on your results. Did you successfully construct the midpoint?

   b. Now calculate the slope of the segment using only the coordinates of the endpoints. (Hint: It might be necessary to use parentheses when you are using the calculator.) Check your results by calculating the slope using the Measure menu. Drag an endpoint of the segment and report on the results of your calculations.

Discovering Geometry with The Geometer's Sketchpad   **25**

Lesson 4.4

Slopes of Parallel and Perpendicular Lines

You have learned how to find the slopes of any line or segment. In this investigation, you'll learn the relationships between parallel lines and their slopes and between perpendicular lines and their slopes.

Investigation 4.4.1: Lines with Equal Slopes

Sketch

Step 1   In a new sketch, construct lines *AB* and *CD*. Also construct their point of intersection, *E*.

Step 2   Measure ∠*CEA*.

Step 3   Measure the slopes of $\overleftrightarrow{AB}$ and $\overleftrightarrow{CD}$.

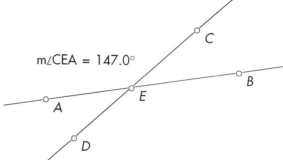

m∠CEA = 147.0°

Investigate

1.   Drag point *D* around point *C* to change the direction of $\overleftrightarrow{CD}$ and observe your measures and calculations. As the measure of ∠*CEA* approaches zero, the lines approach being parallel. You might be able to make the lines exactly parallel, in which case the angle will cease to exist and its measure will disappear. Drag *D* to make the slope measurements equal. What can you conclude about two lines that have equal slopes?

Investigation 4.4.2: Parallel Lines

Sketch (Continued)

Step 4   In the same sketch, drag point *D* so the slopes of $\overleftrightarrow{AB}$ and $\overleftrightarrow{CD}$ are no longer equal. Now construct a new line through *C* parallel to $\overleftrightarrow{AB}$.

Step 5   Measure the slope of the new line.

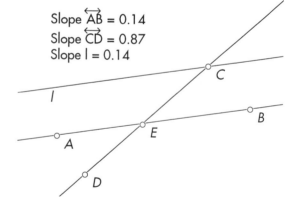

Slope $\overleftrightarrow{AB}$ = 0.14
Slope $\overleftrightarrow{CD}$ = 0.87
Slope l = 0.14

Investigate

2.   Drag point *B*, and observe the slopes. What do you notice about the slopes of two parallel lines?

3.   Write your observations about parallel lines and slopes as a conjecture (C-21: Parallel Slope Conjecture).

Investigation 4.4.3: Perpendicular Lines

Sketch

Step 1   In a new sketch, construct $\overleftrightarrow{AB}$.

Step 2   Construct point *C* above $\overleftrightarrow{AB}$.

Step 3   Construct a line through *C* perpendicular to $\overleftrightarrow{AB}$.

Step 4   Measure the slopes of both lines.

Step 5   Calculate the product of the slopes. (To do this, choose Calculate from the Measure menu. Position the calculator so that you can see the slope measurements in the sketch. Click in the sketch on a slope measurement, then click * in the calculator, and then click in the other slope measurement. If the expression in the calculator looks correct, click OK.)

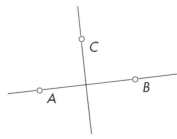

Investigate

4. Drag point *B* and observe the slopes and their product. If two lines are perpendicular, what is the relationship between their slopes?

Investigation 4.4.4: When Are Two Lines Perpendicular?

Except for Step 4, this sketch is similar to the one you made in Investigation 4.4.1.

Sketch

Step 1 In a new sketch, construct lines *AB* and *CD*. Also construct their point of intersection, *E*.

Step 2 Measure ∠*CEA*.

Step 3 Measure the slopes of $\overleftrightarrow{AB}$ and $\overleftrightarrow{CD}$.

Step 4 Calculate the product of the slopes.

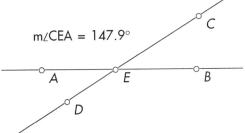

m∠CEA = 147.9°

Investigate

5. Drag *D* until the product of the two slopes equals –1. (This could be hard to do if your measurements are very precise, so use Preferences in the Display menu to change the precision if you need to.) Observe the measure ∠*CEA*. What do you notice about lines with slopes whose product is –1?

6. Combine your observations from the last two investigations to write a conjecture about the slopes of perpendicular lines (C-22: Perpendicular Slope Conjecture).

Lesson 4.5

Equations of Lines

There are many ways of describing a line. You can describe a line as a straight path that extends forever. You can also describe a line as a collection of points that follow a certain rule. Since you often designate points by their x- and y-coordinates, your rule for a line can be an equation containing the variables *x* and *y*. Equations like these—called **linear equations** because they represent lines—have many forms. In this activity, you will investigate linear equations.

Investigation 4.5

Sketch

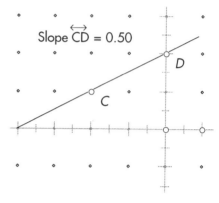

Slope $\overleftrightarrow{CD}$ = 0.50

Step 1   In a new sketch, choose Show Grid from the Graph menu.

Step 2   Draw a line (not a line segment) *CD* so that neither point *C* nor point *D* lies on an axis, then drag point *D* so that it lies on the y-axis.

Step 3   Measure the slope of the line. Drag one of the points on the line and observe how this changes its slope.

Step 4   Use the Measure menu to find the coordinates of point *D* on the y-axis. The y-coordinate of this point is called the **y-intercept** of the line.

Step 5   Now select your line and use the Measure menu to find its equation.

Step 6   Drag your line and compare your three measurements. You may want to turn off Snap to Grid using the Graph menu.

Investigate

1.   One type of linear equation is called the slope-intercept equation. A linear equation is in slope-intercept form if it looks like this:

$$y = mx + b$$

where *m* and *b* are specific values. Describe what *m* and *b* represent, using observations from your sketch.

2.   Now you will create an Action button that allows you to hide the equation of your line. To do this, select the equation, then choose Action Button from the Edit menu, and then Hide/Show. Two buttons should appear on your screen. Double-click the buttons to see how they work. Change the button names to Hide Equation and Show Equation by double-clicking them with the Text tool.

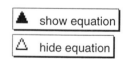

Now hide your equation by double-clicking your new Hide Equation button with the Selection Arrow tool. Drag your line into a new position and predict its new equation. Double-click the Show Equation button to show the equation and test your prediction. Do this a few times. How good were your predictions?

3. Make a Hide/Show button for the slope and a Hide/Show button for the coordinates of the point on the *y*-axis. Drag the line into a new position and predict its new equation with all three measurements hidden. If you are stuck, give yourself hints by showing only one measurement at a time.

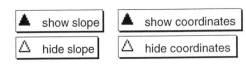

Continue this process with new lines until you can figure out the equation of a line when no measurements at all are showing. Describe your own skill at finding equations of lines.

Explore More

1. Suppose a pair of parallel lines have *y*-intercepts that are two units apart. Does this mean that the lines are two units apart from each other? Construct such a pair of lines to investigate this question. Explain how the distance between these parallel lines depends on their slopes.

2. Measure the equation of a line in slope-intercept form. Use the Graph menu to switch your equation form to Standard. Then find the equation of the same line in standard form. Write down both equations and use your algebra skills to demonstrate that the equations are equivalent. Remember that the computer must round most of its measurements!

Triangle Properties

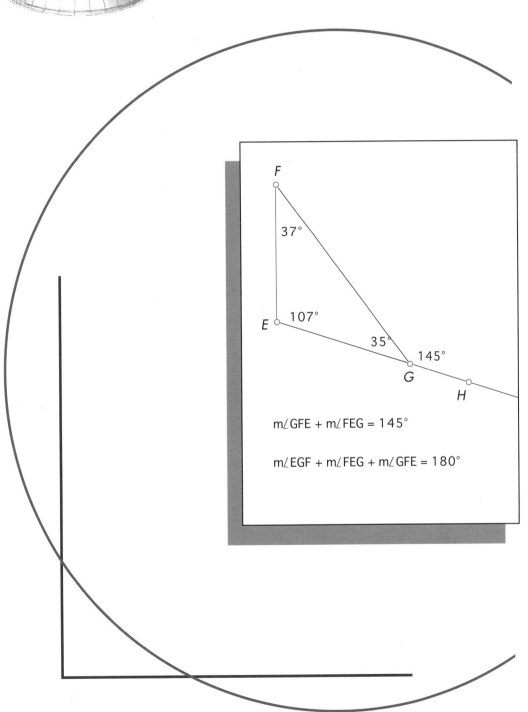

m∠GFE + m∠FEG = 145°

m∠EGF + m∠FEG + m∠GFE = 180°

Lesson 5.1

Triangle Sum Conjecture

In this lesson, you'll investigate and make a conjecture about the sum of the measures of the angles in a triangle.

Investigation 5.1.1

Sketch

Step 1   Draw △*ABC*.

Step 2   Measure ∠*CAB*, ∠*CBA*, and ∠*ACB*. To measure an angle, select three points on the angle, making sure the vertex is in the middle, and then choose Angle in the Measure menu.

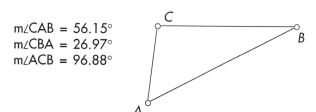

m∠CAB = 56.15°
m∠CBA = 26.97°
m∠ACB = 96.88°

Step 3   Calculate the sum of *m*∠*CAB* + *m*∠*CBA* + *m*∠*ACB*. To do this, double click on one of the measures. Click in the sketch on each angle measurement to add it to your calculation.

Investigate

1.   Drag points *A, B,* and *C*. What do you observe about the sum of the three angles?

2.   Write a conjecture about the sum of the three angles of a triangle (C-25: Triangle Sum Conjecture).

Explore More

1.   Draw a triangle and construct a line through one vertex parallel to the opposite side.

      a. How do the three angles formed at the vertex compare with the angles in the triangle?

      b. Explain how the Triangle Sum Conjecture follows logically from the Parallel Lines Conjecture.

2.   Construct the polygon interior of △*ABC*. Mark *AC* as a vector and translate the triangle and its interior by vector *AC*.

      a. What would fill the space between your two triangles? Construct the midpoint of $\overline{BC}$, mark it as center, and rotate the interior of △*ABC* 180° about this point.

      b. What can you say about the three angles that now meet at a single point (point *C* of the original triangle)?

      c. How does this confirm the Triangle Sum Conjecture?

3.   Investigate angle sums in other polygons.

4.   Find another way to use Sketchpad to demonstrate the Triangle Sum Conjecture.

Lesson 5.2

Discovering Properties of Isosceles Triangles

In this activity, you'll learn how to construct an **isosceles triangle** (a triangle with at least two sides the same length). Then you'll discover properties of isosceles triangles.

Investigation 5.2.1

Sketch

In this sketch, you will construct a triangle that has two sides of equal length and investigate the measures of the base angles.

Step 1   Construct a circle with center A and control point B.

Step 2   Construct radius AB.

Step 3   Construct radius AC. Drag point C to make sure the radius is attached to the circle.

Step 4   Construct $\overline{BC}$.

Step 5   Hide circle AB.

Investigate

1.   Drag each of the vertices of your triangle. Explain why the triangle is always isosceles.

2.   Measure $\angle ACB$ and $\angle ABC$. To measure an angle, select three points on the angle. Make sure the vertex is the middle point. Choose Angle in the Measure menu. Angles ACB and ABC are the **base angles** of the isosceles triangle. Angle CAB is the **vertex angle**. Drag the vertices of your triangle and observe the measures of $\angle ABC$ and $\angle ACB$. What do you observe about the measures?

3.   Write a conjecture about the base angles of an isosceles triangle (C-27: Isosceles Triangle Conjecture).

Investigation 5.2.2

Sketch

In this sketch, you will construct a triangle that has base angles of equal measure and investigate the measures of the sides.

Step 1   In a new sketch, construct $\overleftrightarrow{AB}$.

Step 2   Use the ray tool to construct $\overrightarrow{AC}$ to form acute $\angle CAB$.

Step 3   Mark $\angle CAB$ as an angle of rotation. To do this, select, in order, points C, A, and B. Choose Mark Angle in the Transform menu.

Step 4   Double-click on point B to mark it as a center for rotation.

Step 5   Select $\overleftrightarrow{AB}$ and choose Rotate in the Transform menu. Rotate $\overleftrightarrow{AB}$ by the marked angle.

Step 6   Construct the point of intersection D of this ray and $\overrightarrow{AC}$.

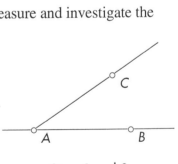

Steps 1 and 2

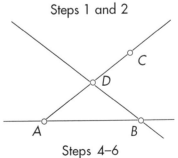

Steps 4–6

Step 7   Hide the two rays and the line.

Step 8   Use the segment tool to construct △ADB.

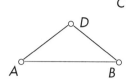

Investigate

4.   Drag point *C* to change the measure of ∠*CAB*. What do you observe about △*ADB*?

5.   Measure the sides of △*ADB*. To measure the length of a segment, select the segment and choose Length in the Measure menu. Drag point *C*. What do you observe about the lengths of $\overline{AD}$ and $\overline{BD}$?

6.   What do you observe about a triangle that has two angles of equal measure? Write your findings as a conjecture (C-28: Converse of the Isosceles Triangle Conjecture).

Explore More

1.   Use Sketchpad to investigate the statement *if a triangle is equiangular, then it is equilateral* and its converse *if a triangle is equilateral, then it is equiangular.* Can you construct an equiangular triangle that is not equilateral? Can you construct an equilateral triangle that is not equiangular? Write a conjecture based on your investigation (C-29: Equilateral Triangle Conjecture).

2.   Determine if it is possible to divide any triangle into two isosceles triangles and a kite. Make a sketch and describe your method.

3.   Construct a triangle such that the measure of one acute angle is half the measure of another acute angle in the triangle. Can the triangle be divided into two isosceles triangles? Make a sketch and explain.

Lesson 5.3

Triangle Inequalities

In this investigation, you'll discover relationships among the measures of the sides and angles in a triangle.

Investigation 5.3.1

Sketch

In this sketch, you will determine whether you can construct a triangle from any three segments.

Step 1 Draw a triangle.

Step 2 Display the segment labels and don't display the point labels.

Step 3 Measure the length of the three sides. To measure a side, select it and choose Length in the Measure menu.

Step 4 Calculate the sum of any two side lengths. To do this, choose Calculate in the Measure menu. Click in the sketch on each segment measurement to add it to your calculation.

m = 1.925 cm
n = 1.941 cm
p = 1.729 cm
m + n = 3.865 cm

Investigate

1. Drag a vertex of the triangle to try to make the sum you calculated equal to the length of the third side. What happens to the triangle?

2. Do you think that it's possible for the sum of the lengths of any two sides of a triangle to be less than the length of the third side? Explain.

3. Summarize your findings as a conjecture about the sum of the lengths of two sides of a triangle (C-30: Triangle Inequality Conjecture).

Investigation 5.3.2

Sketch

In this sketch, you can use △ABC from Investigation 5.3.1.

Step 1 Construct △ABC.

Step 2 Measure ∠ABC, ∠CBA, and ∠ACB.

Step 3 Measure $\overline{AB}$, $\overline{BC}$, and $\overline{CA}$.

Investigate

4. Drag the vertices of your triangle. Copy and fill in the chart below with the name of the angle with the greatest or least measure.

$\overline{AB}$ longest side	Greatest angle? ∠C	$\overline{AC}$ longest side	Greatest angle?____	$\overline{BC}$ longest side	Greatest angle?_____
$\overline{AB}$ shortest side	Least angle?____	$\overline{AC}$ shortest side	Least angle?____	$\overline{BC}$ shortest side	Least angle?_____

5. Write your findings in question 4 as a conjecture (C-31: Side-Angle Inequality Conjecture).

Investigation 5.3.3

Sketch

In this sketch, you will investigate the measure of the exterior angle of a triangle.

Step 1   Draw $\overrightarrow{AB}$.

Step 2   Construct $\triangle ABC$.

Step 3   Construct point D on $\overrightarrow{AB}$ outside the triangle.

Step 4   Measure $\angle CAB$, $\angle ACB$, and $\angle CBD$.

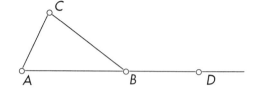

Investigate

6.   Calculate the sum of $\angle CAB + \angle ACB$. Drag point C. What do you observe? Write your findings as a conjecture (C-32: Triangle Exterior Angle Conjecture).

Explore More

1.   Can you form a quadrilateral from any four segments? What must be true about the four segments if they can form a quadrilateral? Investigate.

2.   Investigate inequalities in the medians or altitudes of a triangle. Write your findings or conjectures.

Lesson 5.4

SSS, SAS, and SSA Congruence Shortcuts?

In this investigation, you will investigate three congruence conjectures.

Investigation 5.4.1: SSS

If the three sides in one triangle are congruent to three sides in another triangle (SSS), must the two triangles be congruent? In this investigation, you will test this.

Sketch

Step 1   Open the sketch SSS (Mac) or ch05\sss.gsp (Windows).

Try to connect the points labeled B in the broken triangles.
Can you make triangles that aren't congruent?

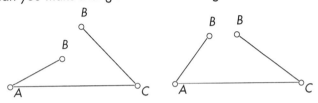

What can you say about triangles whose corresponding three sides are congruent?

Givens:

SSS Sketch

Step 2   Drag the points labeled *B* in the broken triangle on the left so that they coincide to form a triangle.

Step 3   In the broken triangle on the right, try to make the points labeled *B* coincide so that the triangle formed is not congruent to the triangle on the left.

Step 4   Change the length of one or more of the "given" sides (the free segments below the triangles) and try the experiment again.

Investigate

1. Could you form triangles with different sizes or shapes given the three sides?

2. If you were given two triangles with three pairs of congruent sides, would that be enough information to determine that the triangles were congruent?

3. Write a conjecture that summarizes your findings (C-33: SSS Congruence Conjecture).

Investigation 5.4.2: SAS

If the two sides and the angle between them in one triangle are congruent to two sides and the angle between them in another triangle (SAS), must the two triangles be congruent? In this investigation, you will test this.

Sketch

Step 1   Open the sketch called SAS (Mac) or ch05\sas.gsp (Windows).

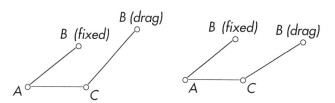

Try to connect the points labeled B in the broken triangles. Can you make two triangles that aren't congruent?

Givens:

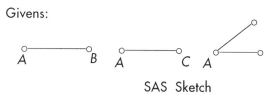

SAS Sketch

Step 2   Drag the point labeled *B* (drag) in the broken triangle on the left so that it coincides with the other point *B* to form a triangle.

Step 3   In the broken triangle on the right, try to make the points labeled *B* coincide so that the triangle formed is not congruent to the triangle on the left.

Step 4   Change the length of one or more of the "given" sides or the measure of the "given" angle (the free segments and the angle below the triangles) and try the experiment again.

Investigate

4.   Could you form two triangles with different sizes or shapes given the two sides and the angle between them?

5.   If you were given two triangles such that two sides and the angle between them in one triangle were congruent to two sides and the angle between them in the other triangle (SAS), would that be enough information to determine that the triangles were congruent?

6.   Write a conjecture that summarizes your findings (C-34: SAS Congruence Conjecture).

Investigation 5.4.3: SSA

If the two sides and an angle not between them in one triangle are congruent to two sides and an angle not between them in another triangle (SSA), must the two triangles be congruent? In this investigation, you will test this.

Sketch

Step 1   Open the sketch called SSA (Mac) or ch05\ssa.gsp (Windows).

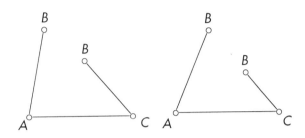

Try to connect the points labeled B in the broken triangles. Can you create two non-congruent triangles?

How many triangles can be formed given two sides and the angle not between them?

Givens:

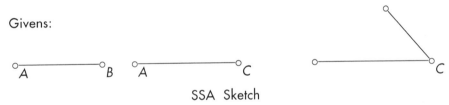

SSA Sketch

Step 2   Drag the points labeled *B* in the broken triangle on the left so that they coincide to form a triangle.

Step 3   In the broken triangle on the right, try to make the points labeled *B* coincide so that the triangle formed is not congruent to the triangle on the left.

Step 4   Change the length of one or more of the "given" sides or the measure of the "given" angle (the free segments and the angle below the triangles) and try the experiment again.

Investigate

7.   Could you form triangles with different sizes or shapes given the two sides and an angle not between them?

8.   If you were given two triangles such that two sides and an angle not between them in one triangle were congruent to two sides and an angle not between them in the other triangle (SSA), would that be enough information to determine that the triangles were congruent?

9.   Summarize your findings.

Lesson 5.5

ASA, SAA, and AAA Congruence Shortcuts?

In this investigation, you will investigate two congruence conjectures.

Investigation 5.5.1: ASA

If two angles and the side between them in one triangle are congruent to two angles and the side between them in another triangle (ASA), must the two triangles be congruent? In this investigation, you will test this.

Sketch

Step 1   Open the sketch called ASA (Mac) or ch05\asa.gsp (Windows).

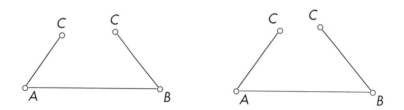

Try to connect the points labeled C in the broken triangles.
Can you make triangles that aren't congruent?

Givens:

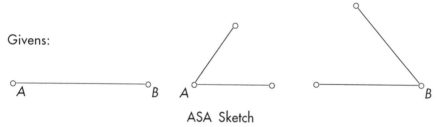

ASA Sketch

Step 2   Drag the points labeled *C* in the broken triangle on the left so that they coincide to form a triangle.

Step 3   In the broken triangle on the right, try to make the points labeled *C* coincide so that the triangle formed is not congruent to the triangle on the left.

Step 4   Change the measure of one or more of the "given" angles or the "given" side (the angles and the segment below the triangles) and try the experiment again.

Investigate

1.   Could you form triangles with different sizes or shapes given the two angles and the side between them?

2.   If you were given two triangles such that two angles and the side between them in one triangle were congruent to two angles and the side between them in another triangle (ASA), would that be enough information to determine that the triangles were congruent?

3.   Write a conjecture that summarizes your findings (C-35: ASA Congruence Conjecture).

Investigation 5.5.3: AAA

If the three angles of one triangle are congruent to the three angles in another triangle (AAA), must the two triangles be congruent? In this investigation, you will test this.

Sketch

Step 1   Open the sketch called AAA (Mac) or ch05\aaa.gsp (Windows).

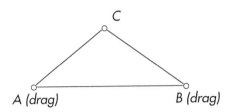

Drag points A and B in the triangle.
Does the triangle maintain its shape and size?

How many triangles can be formed given three angles?

Givens:

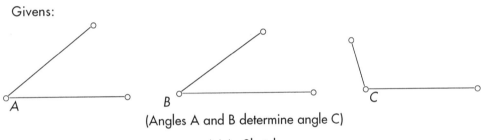

(Angles A and B determine angle C)

AAA Sketch

Step 2   Drag the points labeled *A* and *B* in the triangle.

Step 3   Change the measure of one or more of the "given" angles (the free angles below the triangles) and try the experiment again.

Investigate

4.   Could you form two or more triangles with different sizes or shapes given the three angles?

5.   If you were given two triangles such that the three angles in one triangle were congruent to the three angles in the other triangle (AAA), would that be enough information to determine that the triangles were congruent?

6.   Summarize your findings.

Lesson 5.7

Isosceles Triangles Revisited

In this investigation, you will construct and investigate the properties of the angle bisector, altitude, and median of the vertex angle of isosceles triangles.

Investigation 5.7

Sketch

Construct isosceles $\triangle ABC$ and the angle bisector of the vertex angle.

Step 1   Construct circle AB.

Step 2   Construct radius AB.

Step 3   Construct radius AC. Drag point C to make sure it is attached to the circle.

Step 4   Construct $\overline{BC}$.

Step 5   Hide circle AB.

Step 6   Construct the angle bisector of $\angle CAB$. To do this, select, in order, points C, A, and B. Choose Angle Bisector in the Construct menu.

Step 7   Construct $\overline{AD}$ at the point where the angle bisector intersects the triangle.

Step 8   Hide the ray that forms the angle bisector.

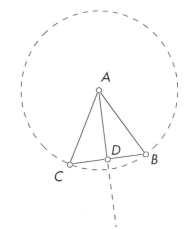

Investigate

1.   Segment AD is the angle bisector segment of the vertex angle of $\triangle ABC$. Is there anything else special about it? To investigate, measure angles ADB and ADC. These measures indicate that $\overline{AD}$ is what kind of special segment?

2.   Measure $\overline{BD}$ and $\overline{DC}$. What is special about point D?

3.   Your answer to question 2 demonstrates that $\overline{AD}$ is also what kind of special segment?

4.   Combine your answers to questions 1, 2, and 3 to write a conjecture about three special segments in an isosceles triangle (C-37: Vertex Angle Bisector Conjecture).

Explore More

1.   Is the converse of your conjecture true? Draw $\triangle ABC$. Construct the angle bisector, the vertex, and the median of one angle. Drag the vertex until the three lines coincide. What kind of triangle is $\triangle ABC$? Investigate.

2.   Construct isosceles $\triangle ABC$. Construct the angle bisector, median, and altitude of a nonvertex angle of your isosceles triangle. Try to make these three lines concurrent. Make a conjecture based on your findings.

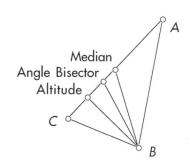

Polygon Properties

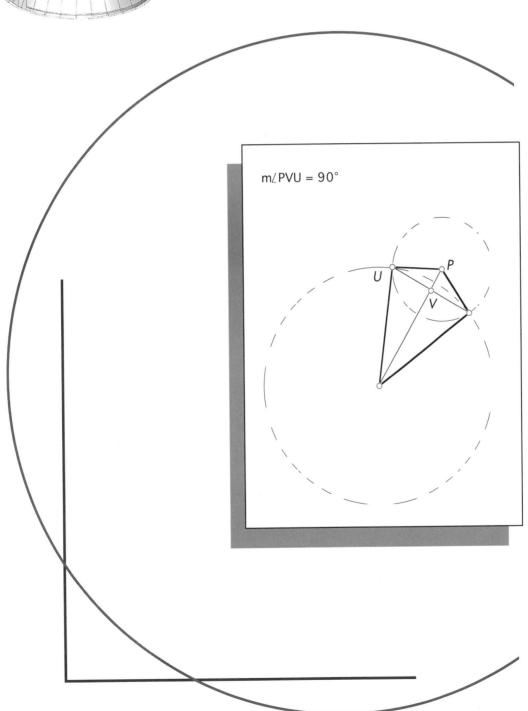

m∠PVU = 90°

Lesson 6.1

Polygon Sum Conjecture

You discovered that the angle measures of any triangle always add to the same number. Do you think that the same will be true for other polygons? In this activity, you will find out.

Investigation 6.1

Sketch

Step 1   Construct a quadrilateral.

Step 2   Measure the four angles of the quadrilateral. (To measure an angle, select three points on the angle, with the vertex your middle selection, and then choose Angle in the Measure menu.)

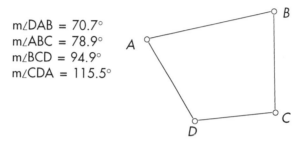

m∠DAB = 70.7°
m∠ABC = 78.9°
m∠BCD = 94.9°
m∠CDA = 115.5°

Step 3   Sum all the angle measures using the calculator. (Click a measurement in the sketch to input it into the calculator.)

Investigate

1.   Drag vertices of the quadrilateral and observe the angle sum. For now, just consider the angle sum in convex quadrilaterals. Record your observations as a conjecture (C-38: Quadrilateral Sum Conjecture).

Now you can extend your conjecture about quadrilaterals to make conjectures about polygons with more than four sides. Before you get started, you need to decide a few things in your group.

2.   There are many different types of polygons with more than four sides—pentagons, hexagons, octagons, and so on. In your group, decide which polygon your group would like to investigate. You may want to make sure that no other group is investigating the same polygon.

   a. Let n represent the number of sides of your polygon. Record n.

   b. Give the name of the polygon if it has one.

3.   Before you explore the sum of the angles of your polygon on Sketchpad, predict what you will discover. Record your prediction and explain why you think it is reasonable.

4.   Construct your polygon and calculate the sum of all its angles. Drag different vertices of your polygon and explain whether your sketch confirms your prediction from question 3.

5.   Compare your results with results from groups that investigated other polygons. After you study the different results, write a conjecture that generalizes the sum of the angles for any polygon with n sides (C-39: Polygon Sum Conjecture).

Explore More

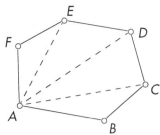

1. Construct a polygon with more than four sides. Use dashed segments to connect one of the vertices to every other vertex. (Since the vertex is already connected to its neighboring vertices, you don't need to construct these segments again.) You have dissected your polygon into triangles. Use this sketch to explain why the Polygon Sum Conjecture follows directly from the Triangle Sum Conjecture.

2. Now you can explore the concave polygons you have ignored so far. *Discovering Geometry* defines an angle's measure to be between 0° and 180°. Sketchpad will give angle measures up to and including 180°, but not greater. By that definition, there's no interior angle at a vertex of a "caved-in" part of a concave polygon. If you consider these points to be vertices of interior angles with measures greater than 180°, does the Polygon Sum Conjecture still hold? Use a polygon like the one from Explore More 1 to investigate this question.

3. Calculate the measure of an angle of a *regular* octagon. Use this information to construct a regular octagon by repeatedly rotating a segment by this angle. Save or print your regular octagon.

Lesson 6.2

Exterior Angles of a Polygon

You form an exterior angle of a polygon when you extend one of the polygon's sides. Exterior angles lie outside the polygon. In this investigation, you'll discover the sum of the measures of the exterior angles in a polygon. You will also discover a formula for finding the interior angle of any equiangular polygon.

Investigation 6.2A: The Sum of the Exterior Angles of a Polygon

Sketch

An efficient way to experiment with different polygons is for different groups to explore different ones. This way, you can combine your results when you are done to make a conjecture about more than one type of polygon. Start with the simplest polygons and pick either a triangle, a quadrilateral, or a pentagon, making sure that other groups are investigating the other two types. Of course, if you want, you can pick a polygon with more sides.

The pictures here show the construction steps for a quadrilateral. Since the steps are essentially the same for any polygon, don't let the pictures confuse you if you have picked a different one.

Step 1   Use the ray tool to construct the polygon and its exterior angles so that it is similar to the diagram on the right. Make sure your polygon is convex. (Note: This construction creates only one set of exterior angles. You would construct a different set if you went in the opposite direction with your rays.)

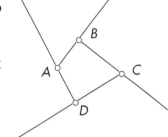

Step 2   Add a point to every ray on the part that extends beyond the polygon. These points are necessary for measuring the exterior angles.

Step 3   Measure all the exterior angles. Make sure you measure the correct angles! You should measure as many angles as there are sides to your polygon. (To measure an angle, select three points on the angle, making sure the vertex is in the middle, and choose Angle in the Display menu.)

Step 4   Calculate the sum of the exterior angles. (Click on the measurement in the sketch to input it into the calculator.)

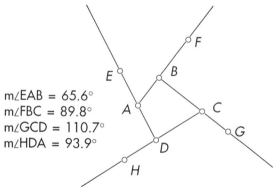

m∠EAB = 65.6°
m∠FBC = 89.8°
m∠GCD = 110.7°
m∠HDA = 93.9°

Investigate

1. Drag vertices of your polygon to see if the sum changes. (Make sure your polygon remains convex.) Record your observations.

2. Compare your results with other results in your class. After comparing the exterior angle sums of different polygons, write the Exterior Angle Sum Conjecture (C-40).

Investigation 6.2B: Constructing Regular Polygons

Your knowledge about angles of polygons will help you construct regular polygons. Recall that a regular polygon is both equilateral and equiangular. For this investigation, it is more interesting to use polygons with many sides.

Investigate

3. Pick a polygon with more than five sides. Assume your polygon is equiangular, and figure out the measure of an interior angle. Record your results and explain your method.

Sketch

Step 1   Construct a segment.

Step 2   Double-click an endpoint of the segment to mark it as a center of rotation.

Step 3   Rotate the segment by the angle you figured out in question 3. (To do this, select the segment and its other endpoint and choose Rotate in the Transform menu. Then type in the appropriate angle measurement.)

Step 4   Figure out how to construct the rest of your regular polygon.

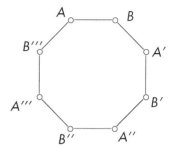

An equiangular octagon

Investigate

4. Find a formula that will calculate the measure of an interior angle for any equiangular *n*-gon. It will help to first compare the angle in your construction with angles in other polygons around your class. Write your formula in the form of a conjecture (C-41: Equiangular Polygon Conjecture).

5. Is the equiangular polygon that you constructed also equilateral?

6. Describe an equiangular polygon that is not equilateral.

Explore More

1. Repeat step 1 of the sketch in Investigation 6.2A, or use your old sketch if you still have it. Mark any point as a center. Select All; then use the Dilate tool to drag the selection toward the center point. (To get the Dilate tool, hold down the Selection Arrow tool and choose the tool on the far right.) Write a paragraph to describe your observations. Use these questions to help you:

   As your polygon gets smaller and smaller, what happens to the exterior angles?

   What can you say about the angles as the polygon approaches a single point?

   How does this illustrate your Exterior Angle Conjecture?

2. Construct a polygon that is always equiangular but not always equilateral.

Lesson 6.3

Discovering Kite and Trapezoid Properties

You learned the definitions of different kinds of quadrilaterals in Chapter 2. Keep these definitions handy, since you may need to refer to them. In the next few lessons, you will learn more about the properties of different quadrilaterals. In this activity, you will discover properties of kites and trapezoids.

Investigation 6.3.1: Properties of a Kite

Sketch

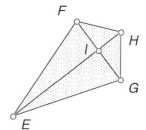

Step 1   Open the sketch Quad Family (Mac) or ch06\quadfmly.gsp (Windows). Drag different vertices of the quadrilaterals and determine which quadrilateral is the kite. You will use this quadrilateral for the rest of this investigation, so drag it to another part of the screen and make it large. If you prefer, you can copy it and paste it into a new sketch.

Step 2   Construct both diagonals of the kite.

Step 3   Construct the point of intersection of the diagonals.

Investigate

1.   Drag vertices of the kite and observe how the diagonals intersect. Measure an angle formed by the diagonals to check your observations. Record your observations as the Kite Diagonals Conjecture (C-42). (To measure an angle in Sketchpad, select three points on the angle, making sure that the vertex is in the middle. Then choose Angle in the Measure menu.)

2.   The **vertex angles** of a kite are the angles formed by pairs of congruent sides. Decide which diagonal connects the vertex angles of the kite. Then observe how this diagonal divides the other diagonal. Drag vertices and measure distances to check your observations. Then record your observations as the Kite Diagonal Bisector Conjecture (C-43). (To measure a distance between points, select the two points and choose Distance from the Measure menu.)

3.   Measure all four angles of your kite. Drag vertices of the kite and observe the measures of the vertex angles and the nonvertex angles. Record your observations as the Kite Angles Conjecture (C-44).

4.   The diagonals divide each angle of the kite into two new angles. Drag vertices of the kite and make observations about how each diagonal divides the vertex angles and the nonvertex angles. Measure some of the smaller angles to check your observations. Record them as the Kite Angle Bisector Conjecture (C-45).

Investigation 6.3.2: Properties of a Trapezoid

Sketch

Step 1   Look back at the sketch Quad Family (Mac) or ch06\quadfmly.gsp (Windows). Drag different vertices of the remaining quadrilaterals and determine which quadrilateral is a trapezoid. In an **isosceles trapezoid**, the two nonparallel sides are the same length. Do not use the isosceles trapezoid until the next investigation. Since you will use the ordinary trapezoid for the rest of this investigation, drag it to another part of the screen and make it large. If you prefer, you can copy it and paste it into a new sketch.

Step 2   Measure all four angles of the trapezoid.

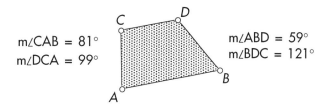

m∠CAB = 81°
m∠DCA = 99°

m∠ABD = 59°
m∠BDC = 121°

Investigate

5. The two parallel sides of the trapezoid are called bases. Find a pair of consecutive angles that lie between the bases. There are two such pairs. Rearrange your angle measurements so that they are paired up to match these consecutive pairs. Drag vertices of the trapezoid and observe the angle pairs. Make calculations to check your observations. Then write your observations as the Trapezoid Consecutive Angles Conjecture (C-46).

Investigation 6.3.3: Properties of an Isosceles Trapezoid

Sketch

Step 1   Look back at the sketch Quad Family (Mac) or ch06\quadfmly.gsp (Windows). Drag different parts of the remaining quadrilaterals and find the isosceles trapezoid.

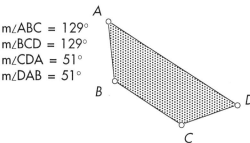

m∠ABC = 129°
m∠BCD = 129°
m∠CDA = 51°
m∠DAB = 51°

Step 2   Measure all four angles of the trapezoid.

Investigate

6. Drag different vertices of the isosceles trapezoid and observe the angle measures. Write your observations as the Isosceles Trapezoid Conjecture (C-47).

7. Construct the diagonals of the isosceles trapezoid and measure both of their lengths. Drag vertices of the trapezoid and make observations about their lengths. Write your observations as the Isosceles Trapezoid Diagonals Conjecture (C-48).

m $\overline{AC}$ = 2.26 cm
m $\overline{BD}$ = 2.26 cm

Explore More

For each of these constructions, drag vertices to make sure your construction has enough constraints to always construct the polygon you want. Also make sure your construction doesn't have too many constraints, in which case there may be some versions of the polygon that it cannot represent.

1. Construct a kite.
2. Construct a trapezoid.
3. Construct an isosceles trapezoid.
4. Concave kites are called darts. Check the kite conjectures to see if they hold for darts.

Lesson 6.4

Discovering Properties of Midsegments

When you connect midpoints of certain sides of certain polygons, you create a **midsegment**. In this activity, you will construct midsegments of triangles and of trapezoids and investigate their properties.

Investigation 6.4.1: The Midsegment of a Triangle

Sketch

Step 1   Construct a triangle.

Step 2   Construct the midpoint of each side. (To do this, select each side and choose Point at Midpoint from the Construct menu.)

Step 3   Construct all three midsegments by connecting all the midpoints.

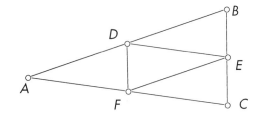

Investigate

1. Drag vertices of your original triangle and observe the four smaller triangles. Do they appear congruent? Make appropriate measurements to check your observations. Then record your observations about the four smaller triangles as a conjecture (C-49).

2. Select a midsegment and change its line weight to thick using the Display menu. Now find the side of the original triangle that the midsegment is not connected to and make that side thick as well. Before making any measurements, drag a vertex of your original triangle and make predictions about relationships between the midsegment and this third side.

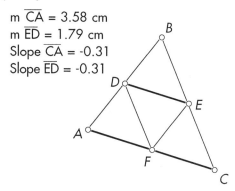

3. Now measure the length and slope of both thick segments. Drag vertices of the original triangle and compare the slopes and lengths of these segments. Record your observations as the Triangle Midsegment Conjecture (C-50).

Investigation 6.4.2: The Midsegment of a Trapezoid

Sketch

Step 1   Open up the sketch Quad Family (Mac) or ch06\quadfmly.gsp (Windows). Drag different parts of the quadrilaterals and determine which quadrilateral is the trapezoid. (Do *not* use the isosceles trapezoid.) You will use this quadrilateral for the rest of this investigation, so drag it to another part of the screen and make it large. If you prefer, you can copy it and paste it into a new sketch.

Step 2   The midsegment of a trapezoid is the segment connecting the midpoints of the nonparallel sides. Construct the midsegment of your trapezoid.

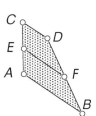

Investigate

Slope $\overline{CD}$ = 0.10
Slope $\overline{EF}$ = 0.10
Slope $\overline{AB}$ = 0.10

m $\overline{CD}$ = 2.7 cm
m $\overline{EF}$ = 3.1 cm
m $\overline{AB}$ = 3.5 cm

4. Measure the slopes of the midsegment and the parallel sides. Drag vertices of your trapezoid and write a conjecture based on your observations.

5. Now measure the lengths of the midsegment and the parallel sides. Make a guess about how the length of the midsegment compares to the lengths of the parallel sides. Check your guess using Sketchpad's calculator. Record your observations as a second conjecture about the midsegment of a trapezoid. (You may need to use parentheses when you use Sketchpad's calculator.)

6. Now combine your results from your last two conjectures to make a single conjecture about the midsegment of a trapezoid (C-51: Trapezoid Midsegment Conjecture).

Lesson 6.5

Discovering Properties of Parallelograms

A **parallelogram** is a quadrilateral whose opposite sides are parallel. In this activity, you will investigate properties of parallelograms.

Investigation 6.5

Sketch

First, you will construct a parallelogram using the definition.

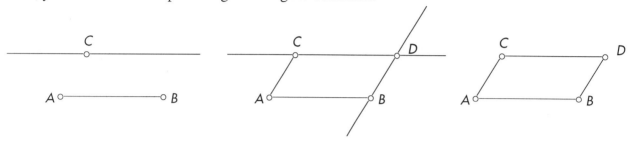

| Steps 1 and 2 | Steps 3–5 | Step 6 |

Step 1   Construct segment AB and point C above the segment.

Step 2   Construct a line through C parallel to segment AB. (To do this, select the segment and the point and choose Parallel Line in the Construct menu.)

Step 3   Construct segment AC.

Step 4   Construct a line through B parallel to segment AC.

Step 5   Construct the point of intersection of the two lines. Label the point D.

Step 6   Hide both lines, and finish your parallelogram by constructing the missing segments.

Step 7   Drag different vertices of your parallelogram to check to make sure you constructed it properly.

Investigate

1.   Measure all four angles of your parallelogram. (To measure an angle, select three points on the angle, making sure that the vertex is the middle point. Then choose Angle from the Measure menu.) Drag vertices to observe these angle measures, and then write a conjecture about opposite angles in a parallelogram (C-52).

2.   Add the measures of pairs of consecutive angles in your parallelogram. (Click on the measures to input them into the calculator.) Drag vertices to observe these angle sums, and then write a conjecture about consecutive angles in a parallelogram (C-53).

3.   Measure the lengths of all four sides of your parallelogram. Drag vertices to observe these lengths, and then write a conjecture about opposite sides in a parallelogram (C-54).

4.   Construct the diagonals of your parallelogram and their point of intersection. Label this point E. Measure AE, ED, CE, and EB. Drag vertices to observe these lengths, and then write a conjecture about the diagonals in a parallelogram (C-55).

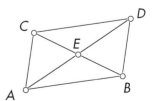

Explore More

Find other ways to construct a parallelogram, using the properties you discovered.

Lesson 6.6

Discovering Properties of Special Parallelograms

You have discovered some properties that hold true for any parallelogram. Now you will discover some properties that are true only for special types of parallelograms.

Investigation 6.6.2: Properties of a Rhombus

A **rhombus** is a parallelogram with four congruent sides.

Sketch

Step 1   Open up the sketch Quad Family (Mac) or ch06\quadfmly.gsp (Windows). Drag different vertices of the quadrilaterals and determine which quadrilateral is always a rhombus (but is not always a square). You will use this quadrilateral for the rest of this investigation, so drag it to another part of the screen and make it large. If you prefer, you can copy it into a new sketch.

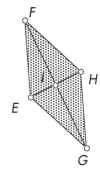

Step 2   Construct the diagonals of the rhombus.

Step 3   Construct the point of intersection of the diagonals.

Investigate

Steps 1–3

1.   Drag the vertices of the rhombus and observe the diagonals. You should notice two different properties that describe how the diagonals intersect. Make measurements to verify your observations. Then write them as a conjecture (C-57).

2.   Now drag different vertices and observe how each diagonal intersects the angles of the rhombus. Make some angle measurements to verify your observations. Then write your observations as a conjecture (C-58).

Investigation 6.6.3A: Properties of a Rectangle

A **rectangle** is an equiangular parallelogram.

Sketch

Step 1   Look back at the sketch Quad Family (Mac) or ch06\quadfmly.gsp (Windows). Drag different vertices of the quadrilaterals and determine which quadrilateral is always a rectangle (but is not always a square). You will use this quadrilateral for the rest of this investigation, so drag it to another part of the screen and make it large. If you prefer, you can copy it into a new sketch.

Step 2   Measure at least two of the angles of the rectangle. (You probably won't need to bother measuring the others.)

Investigate

3.   Drag vertices of the rectangle and write a conjecture about the measure of its angles (C-59).

4.   Construct both diagonals of the rectangle. Drag vertices of the rectangle and observe the diagonals. Make measurements to verify your observations. Then write a conjecture about the diagonals of a rectangle (C-60).

Investigation 6.6.3B: Properties of a Square

Sketch

Go back to the sketch Quad Family (Mac) or ch06\quadfmly.gsp (Windows). Drag different vertices of the quadrilaterals and determine which quadrilateral is always a square.

Investigate

5. Test the conjectures you made for rhombuses and rectangles (C-57 through C-60) on the square. Which of them hold for the square?

6. You may have noticed that you haven't been given a definition of a square. Instead, you will write your own.

    a. First write a definition of a square that uses the word *rhombus*.

    b. Now write a definition of a square that uses the word *rectangle*.

Explore More

Try one or more of the first three constructions below. Drag vertices to make sure your construction has enough constraints so that it is always the polygon you want. Also make sure your construction doesn't have too many constraints, in which case there may be some versions of the polygon that it cannot represent.

1. Construct a rhombus.

2. Construct a rectangle.

3. Construct a square.

4. Construct a parallelogram.

    a. Bisect a pair of opposite angles of the parallelogram. What can you conjecture about these angle bisectors? Try to explain why your conjecture is true.

    b. Follow the same procedure as in part a for a pair of adjacent angles in your parallelogram.

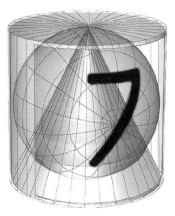

Circles

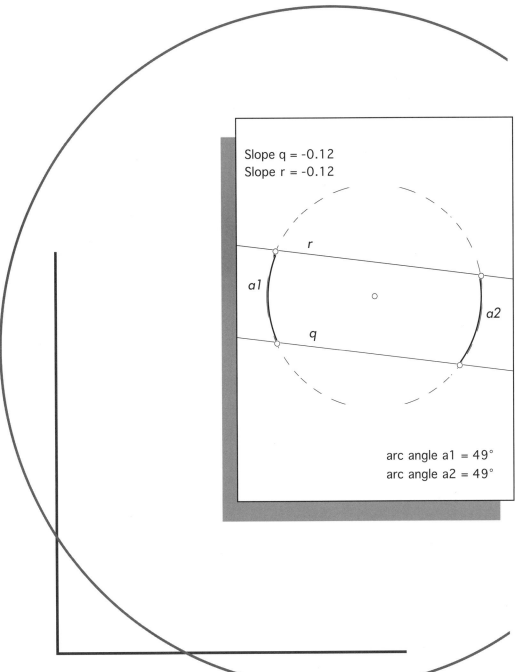

Slope q = -0.12
Slope r = -0.12

r

a1

q

a2

arc angle a1 = 49°
arc angle a2 = 49°

Lesson 7.1

Defining Circles

A **circle** is the set of all points in a plane at a given distance from a given point in the plane. In this activity, you'll construct circles and various lines, angles, and segments associated with circles. You'll answer questions about each construction. In some cases, you'll be asked to define the object you constructed.

Investigation: Defining Circle Terms

Sketch

Step 1   Use the circle tool to construct a circle.

Two points, point A and point B, define your circle. Drag each point to see how it affects the circle. Point A is the center of the circle. Point B controls the circle's radius. In most books, a circle is named after its center point. The circle shown at right would be called circle A. When describing Sketchpad circles, it's often convenient to name a circle after both points that define it, so you could also call the circle at right circle AB.

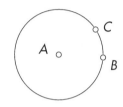

CA = 0.473 inches

Step 2   Construct point C on the circle.

Step 3   Select point A and point C and choose Distance in the Measure menu.

Investigate

1.   Drag point C around the circle. What do you notice about the distance AC? How does this observation relate to the definition of a circle?

2.   Construct segment AB. This segment is called a **radius**. The term *radius* is also used to describe the distance from the center of a circle to any point on the circle. You can change the radius of this circle by dragging point A or point B. One way to measure a circle's radius is to select the circle itself and then choose Radius in the Measure menu. Find and describe two other ways you can measure the radius of a circle using different commands in the Measure menu.

3.   Construct a circle centered at point A with control point D as shown at right. Drag point D so that circle AD goes inside and outside circle AB. If two or more coplanar circles share the same center, they are **concentric** circles. How many circles can share the same center? (Can you see why it might be convenient to name circles after two points?)

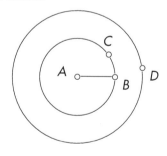

4.   Construct a point E anywhere in your sketch. Select segment AB and point E and choose Circle By Center+Radius in the Construct menu. Drag point B to see how it affects your new circle. Circle E and circle AB are **congruent circles**. Write a definition of *congruent circles*.

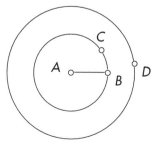

Investigation: Defining Arcs

Sketch

Step 1   In a new sketch, construct circle *AB*.

Step 2   Construct point *C* on the circle.

Step 3   Select, in order, the circle, point *B*, and point *C*. Choose Arc On Circle in the Construct menu. While this arc is selected, change Line Weight to Thick in the Display menu.

Step 4   Select, in order, the circle, point *C* and point *B*. Choose Arc On Circle in the Construct menu. This should give you a different arc from the one you constructed in step 3. Change the color and/or thickness of this arc.

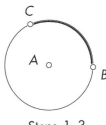

Steps 1–3

Investigate

Two points on a circle divide the circle into two arcs. In the figure at right, one arc from point *B* to point *C* is less than half the circle. This is called a **minor arc**. The other arc, which is more than half the circle, is called a **major arc**. The minor arc is named after its two endpoints: $\overset{\frown}{BC}$ or $\overset{\frown}{CB}$. We use three points to name a major arc. The first and last letters come from the endpoints, and the middle letter is any other point on the arc.

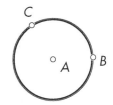

5.   Construct a point *D* on the major arc. (To do this, select the arc and choose Point On Object in the Construct menu.) Write two names for the major arc.

6.   Drag point *C* until it appears that points *B* and *C* divide the circle into congruent halves. An arc that is half a circle is called a **semicircle**. Do you think semicircles should be named by two points or by three? Explain. Name the semicircles in your sketch. Add a point to the sketch, if necessary.

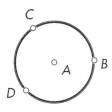

Investigation 7.1: Defining Segments and Lines in Circles

Sketch and Investigate

7.   Open a new sketch. Construct a circle *AB* and a segment *BC*, where point *C* is a point on the circle. Drag point *C* and observe its behavior. Segment *BC* is a **chord** of the circle. Define *chord*.

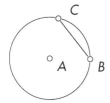

8.   Drag point *C* so that $\overline{BC}$ passes through point *A*. In that position, $\overline{BC}$ is a special chord called a **diameter** of the circle. Define *diameter*.

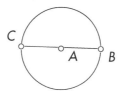

(Note: Like the term *radius*, the term *diameter* can refer to a segment as well as to the length of the segment.)

9.   Construct a line through points *B* and *C*. (The line will overlap $\overline{BC}$.) Drag point *C* again. Line *BC* is a secant of the circle. Define *secant*.

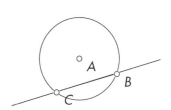

10. Drag point *C* toward point *B* until the two points coincide in a single point. The line is no longer a secant. Instead, it is called a **tangent**. Define *tangent*.

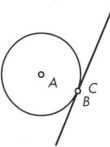

11. Open a new sketch. Construct circle *AB*. Construct points *C* and *D* on the circle. Construct segments *CB* and *CD*. ∠*BCD* is an **inscribed angle**. Define *inscribed angle*.

12. Arrange points *C* and *D* so that $\overset{\frown}{BD}$ is a minor arc and $\overset{\frown}{BCD}$ is a major arc. In the figure at right, inscribed angle *BCD* intercepts arc *BD*. Drag point *C* in your sketch. How many angles can intercept a given arc?

13. Drag point *C* so that it lies on $\overset{\frown}{BD}$. Do you think inscribed angle *BCD* still intercepts $\overset{\frown}{BD}$? What kind of arc does it intercept? Explain.

14. Open a new sketch. Construct circle *AB*. Construct radii $\overline{AB}$ and $\overline{AC}$. Drag point *C*. ∠*CAB* is a **central angle**. Define *central angle*.

Explore More

1. In question 8, you dragged an endpoint of a chord so that it temporarily became a diameter. But you never actually constructed a diameter that would stay a diameter no matter what you dragged. Try it. Construct a circle and a diameter that stays a diameter.

2. In question 10, you dragged a point so that a secant was no longer a secant, temporarily becoming a tangent instead. But you never actually constructed a line that would stay a tangent no matter what you dragged. Try it. Construct a circle and a line that is always tangent to the circle. Hint: Draw a radius first; then think of a relationship between the radius and the tangent line that passes through the endpoint of the radius.

Lesson 7.2

Discovering Chord Properties

In this lesson, you will discover some properties of chords, arcs, and central angles. In Investigation 7.2.1, you'll construct and investigate a pair of congruent chords.

Investigation 7.2.1

Sketch

Step 1   Construct circle *AB*.

Step 2   Construct $\overline{BC}$, where point *C* is a point on the circle.

Step 3   Construct point *D* on the circle.

Step 4   Select $\overline{BC}$ and point *D* and choose Circle By Center+Radius in the Construct menu.

Step 5   Construct $\overline{DE}$ so that point *E* is a point of intersection of this new circle and circle *AB*.

Step 6   Hide the circle centered at point *D*.

Step 7   Construct segments *AB*, *AC*, *AD*, and *AE*.

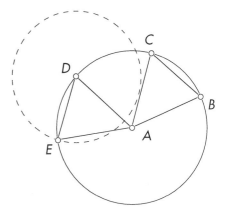

Investigate

1. Drag different parts of your figure to confirm that the chords you constructed stay congruent. Measure central angles *CAB* and *DAE*. (Remember: To measure an angle, hold down Shift and select three points, with the vertex your middle selection.) Write a conjecture about congruent chords in a circle and the central angles they determine (C-61).

2. The measure of a minor arc is defined as the measure of its central angle. Select point *B*, point *C*, and the circle and choose Arc Angle in the Measure menu to confirm this. Measure the arc intercepted by the other chord. What can you conclude about congruent chords in a circle and the arcs they intercept? Write a conjecture (C-62).

3. Measure the distance from point *A* to $\overline{BC}$ and the distance from point *A* to $\overline{DE'}$. (Select a point and a segment and choose Distance in the Measure menu.) Drag parts of your sketch and observe these distances for different pairs of congruent chords. Write a conjecture about congruent chords in a circle and their distances from the circle's center (C-64).

Investigation 7.2.2

Sketch

Step 1   In a new sketch, construct circle *AB*.

Step 2   Construct chord *BC*.

Step 3   Select the chord and point *A* and choose Perpendicular Line in the Construct menu.

Investigate

4. Drag point *C* and observe the relationship between the chord and the perpendicular to it from the center of the circle. At what special point does the perpendicular intersect the chord? Write a conjecture (C-63).

Investigation 7.2.3

Sketch

In this investigation, you'll investigate the converse of the conjecture you made in question 4.

Step 1   In a new sketch, construct circle *AB*.

Step 2   Construct chord *BC*.

Step 3   Construct the midpoint *D* of $\overline{BC}$.

Step 4   Construct a line through point *D*, perpendicular to $\overline{BC}$.

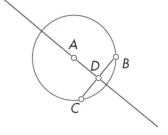

Investigate

5.   What do you notice about the perpendicular bisector of a chord? Drag parts of your sketch to confirm that this is always true; then write a conjecture (C-65).

6.   Hide the center of your circle. Now perform a construction to locate the center. Explain how you did it. (Choosing Show All Hidden is cheating!)

Explore More

1.   Use congruent triangles to explain why C-61 is true.

2.   Make a chord longer without changing the size of the circle. Does the chord get closer to or farther from the center of the circle? Investigate this question. Describe what you did and state your findings as a conjecture.

3.   Suppose a chord in one circle is congruent to a chord in a second circle, but the second circle has a greater radius than the first circle. Do the two chords determine congruent central angles? If not, which central angle has the greater measure? Investigate these questions. Describe what you did and state your findings as a conjecture.

Lesson 7.3

Discovering Tangent Properties

Investigation 7.3.1

In this investigation, you'll discover a relationship between a tangent line and the radius drawn to the point of tangency.

Step 1   Construct circle AB.

Step 2   Construct $\overline{AB}$.

Step 3   Construct line BC, where point C is a point on the circle. (Drag point C to make sure it's properly attached.)

Step 4   Measure $\angle CBA$. (Remember: To measure an angle, select three points, with the vertex in the middle.)

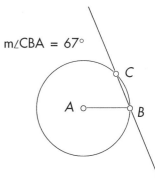

m∠CBA = 67°

Investigate

1.   Drag point C toward point B and watch the angle measure change. When point C coincides with point B, the line will be approximately tangent. What's the measure of $\angle CBA$? Write a conjecture about a tangent and the radius drawn to the point of tangency (C-66: Tangent Conjecture).

Investigation 7.3.2

Investigation 7.3.1 may have given you an idea of how to construct a tangent to a circle. In this investigation, you'll construct two tangents and investigate a relationship between the distances from the points of tangency to the point where the tangents intersect.

Sketch

Step 1   In a new sketch, construct circle AB.

Step 2   Construct $\overline{AB}$.

Step 3   To construct a tangent, select point B and $\overline{AB}$ and choose Perpendicular Line in the Construct menu.

Step 4   Construct $\overline{AC}$, where point C is a point on the circle.

Step 5   Construct a tangent through point C.

Step 6   Construct point D where these tangent lines intersect.

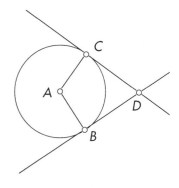

Investigate

2.   The two tangent lines intersect at a point outside the circle to form tangent segments (unless the lines are parallel). Measure BD and CD. (To measure the distance between two points, select the points and choose Distance in the Measure menu.) Drag point C and observe the measurements. Write a conjecture about tangent segments (C-67: Tangent Segments Conjecture).

Explore More

Given a circle and a point outside the circle, find a method for constructing the two tangents from that point. Here's a start: Construct a segment from the point to the circle's center. Construct the midpoint of that segment. You're on your own from here. Describe how you did your construction.

Lesson 7.4

Arcs and Angles

Investigations 7.4.1–7.4.3

In these investigations, you'll discover a relationship between an inscribed angle and the arc it intercepts.

Sketch

Step 1   Construct circle *AB*.

Step 2   Construct $\overline{CB}$, where point *C* is a point on the circle.

Step 3   Construct $\overline{CD}$, where point *D* is another point on the circle.

Step 4   Measure ∠*DCB*. (To measure an angle, select three points, with the vertex your second selection.)

Step 5   Select, in order, point *B*, point *D*, and the circle and choose Arc On Circle in the Construct menu. Change its line weight to thick.

Step 6   Select the arc and choose Arc Angle in the Construct menu.

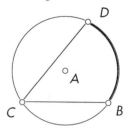

m∠DCB = 50.38°
arc angle a1 = 100.77°

Investigate

1. Drag point *D* (but not past point *C* or point *B*) and look for a relationship between the arc measure (called Arc Angle in Sketchpad) and the measure of the inscribed angle. Make a conjecture (C-68: Inscribed Angle Conjecture).

2. Drag point *C*. As long as you don't drag it past points *B* and *D*, the measures don't change. Is your computer broken? Well, dragging point *C* doesn't do anything to the arc. What does that mean for all the inscribed angles that intercept that arc? If you're not sure, construct and measure another inscribed angle that intercepts $\overset{\frown}{BD}$. Write a conjecture about inscribed angles that intercept the same arc (C-69).

3. Construct segment *DB* and change its line weight to dashed. Drag point *D* until $\overline{DB}$ passes through the circle's center. What's the measure of ∠*DCB*? Now drag point *C* to see if *m*∠*DCB* changes. Write a conjecture about angles inscribed in a semicircle (C-70).

Investigation 7.4.4

In this investigation, you'll apply your previous discoveries to the angles of a quadrilateral inscribed in a circle. Such a quadrilateral is called a **cyclic quadrilateral**.

Sketch

Step 1   Open a new sketch.

Step 2   Construct circle *AB*.

Step 3   Use the Segment tool to construct quadrilateral *BCDE*, where points *C*, *D*, and *E* are also points on the circle.

Step 4   Measure the four angles of the quadrilateral.

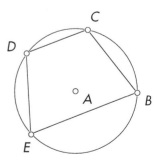

Investigate

4. Look for relationships between pairs of angles in the quadrilateral. Use the calculator to check any relationships you discover, and then write a conjecture (C-71).

5. Explain why C-71 is true. Hints: What kinds of angles did you measure? What is the sum of the arc measures of the two arcs intercepted by opposite angles in the quadrilateral?

Investigation 7.4.5

Next, you'll discover a relationship between arcs formed when parallel lines intersect a circle.

Sketch

Step 1   In a new sketch, construct circle *AB*.

Step 2   Construct $\overleftrightarrow{BC}$, where point *C* is a point on the circle. (Drag points *B* and *C* to make sure the line is attached correctly.)

Step 3   Construct point *D* on the circle.

Step 4   Construct a line through point *D* parallel to $\overleftrightarrow{BC}$.

Step 5   Construct point *E* where the new line intersects the circle.

Step 6   Select, in order, point *E*, point *B*, and the circle. Choose Arc On Circle in the Construct menu. Change the line weight of this arc to thick.

Step 7   Construct $\overarc{CD}$ the same way. Make sure you select your points in a counterclockwise direction.

Investigate

6. Select each arc and measure its arc angle. Drag point *C* and observe the arcs and their measures. Make a conjecture about the arcs intercepted by parallel lines (C-72).

Lesson 7.5

The Circumference/Diameter Ratio

In this lesson, you'll discover a relationship between a circle's circumference and its diameter. Even if that relationship is familiar to you, the investigation may demonstrate it in a different way.

Investigation 7.5

Sketch

Step 1   Construct $\overline{AB}$.

Step 2   Construct point C, the midpoint of $\overline{AB}$.

Step 3   Construct circle CB. Be sure the cursor is positioned directly on point B when you release the mouse button.

Step 4   Measure the circumference of the circle.

Step 5   Measure AB (the diameter of the circle).

Step 6   Make the circle small; then select, in order, the diameter measurement and the circumference measurement and choose Tabulate in the Measure menu.

Step 7   Make the circle a little bigger; then double-click inside the table to add another entry.

Step 8   Repeat step 7 three or four more times.

Circumference ⊙CB = 3.316 inches
m $\overline{AB}$ = 1.056 inches

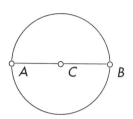

Length(Segment AB)	0.625	1.056
Circumference(Circle CB)	1.964	3.316

Investigate

1.   Click inside the table once to select it; then choose Plot Table Data in the Graph menu. Click Plot in the Plot Points dialog. Describe the points that appear on the graph. If you don't see all of the points, drag the point at $(1, 0)$ to scale your axes.

2.   Construct a ray from the origin of the graph to one of the points on the graph. Measure and record the slope of this ray. What ratio does this slope represent?

3.   Select, in order, the diameter measurement and the circumference measurement. Choose Plot As (x, y) in the Graph menu. Change the color of this point so you can distinguish it from other points on the graph. Drag to change your circle and watch the plotted point. How does this demonstrate that the circumference/diameter ratio is the same for all circles?

4.   Long ago, mathematicians named the circumference/diameter ratio with the Greek letter π (pi). Copy and complete the following conjecture: If C is the circumference and D is the diameter of a circle, then there is a number π such that $C = -?-$. Because $D = 2r$, where r is the radius, then $C = -?-$ (C-73: Circumference Conjecture).

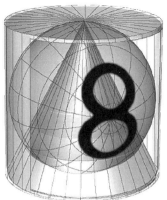

Transformations and Tessellations

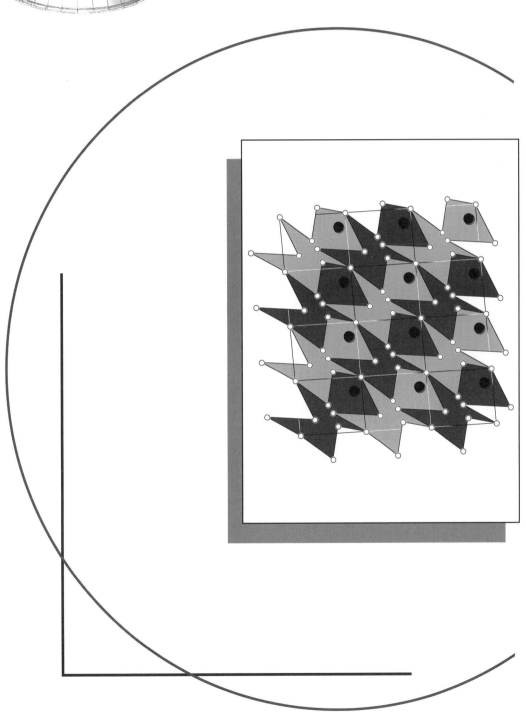

Lesson 8.1

Transformations

A **transformation** is a way of moving or changing an object. There are three types of basic transformations that preserve the size and shape of the object. These three, **reflections**, **rotations**, and **translations**, are called **isometries**. Isometries are also called **rigid transformations** because they move, turn, or reflect an object but never bend or distort it. In this activity, you'll experiment with basic isometries by transforming the letter F.

Sketch

Part 1: Translation

Step 1   Construct the letter *F* and its interior. (One shortcut for constructing this is to: hold down the Shift key and use the Point tool to create the vertices of the letter in order and then choose Polygon Interior in the Measure menu.)

Step 2   In order to translate a shape, you need to indicate a direction and a distance. To do this, construct segment *KL*. Then select, in order, point *K* and point *L*, and choose Mark Vector in the Transform menu.

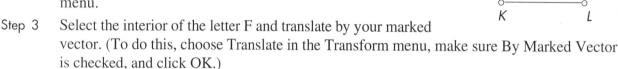

Step 3   Select the interior of the letter F and translate by your marked vector. (To do this, choose Translate in the Transform menu, make sure By Marked Vector is checked, and click OK.)

Step 4   Change the color or shading of the translated image. Use the Text tool to display its label, and change the label to *Translated image*. (To change a label, double-click on the label with the Text tool.)

Step 5   Drag point *L* to change your vector, and observe the relationship between the translated image and the original figure.

Part 2: Rotation

Step 6   In order to rotate a shape, you need to indicate a center of rotation and an angle of rotation. Start by creating angle *MNO* using two attached segments, as indicated at right.

Step 7   Double-click point *N* to mark it as a center of rotation.

Step 8   To mark an angle for rotation, select, in order, point *M*, point *N*, and point *O*. Choose Mark Angle in the Transform menu.

Step 9   Select the original letter *F* and rotate by the angle you marked. (To do this, choose Rotate in the Transform menu, make sure By Marked Angle is checked, and click OK.)

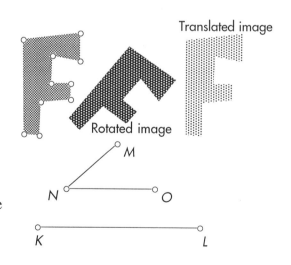

Step 10   Change the color or shading of the rotated image. Also display its label and change the label to *Rotated image*.

Step 11   Drag point *O* to change your angle, and observe the relationship between the rotated image and the original figure.

Part 3: Reflection

Step 12 In order to reflect a shape, you need a **mirror line** (also called a **line of reflection**). Draw a line and label it *Mirror line*.

Step 13 Double-click your line to mark it as a mirror.

Step 14 Reflect the original letter *F*. (To do this, select the interior and choose Reflect in the Transform menu.) Your image may end up off the screen.

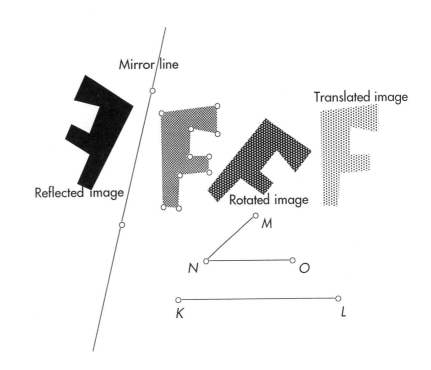

Step 15 Change the color or shading of the reflected image. Label it *Reflected image*.

Step 16 Drag your mirror line, and observe the relationship between the reflected image and the original figure.

Investigate

1. Explain whether it is possible for any of the three images in your sketch to lie directly on top of one another. Experiment by dragging different parts of your sketch.

2. Use the letter *F* and its *translated* image to answer these two questions:
   a. How is the image different from the original?
   b. How is the image the same as the original?

3. Answer questions a and b above for the letter *F* and its *rotated* image.

4. Answer questions a and b above for the letter *F* and its *reflected* image.

Explore More

1. You can indicate transformations on the coordinate plane using an ordered pair rule. For example, the transformation on the right follows the rule $(x, y) \rightarrow (x + 3, y + 1)$. Notice that the translation vector from point *K* to point *L* goes to the right three units and up one unit.

   Choose Show Grid from the Graph menu. Drag the point $(1, 0)$ to scale your axes until the grid is fairly small. Then drag the points of your letter *F* so they fall on grid points. Now drag parts of your sketch so it demonstrates the transformation $(x, y) \rightarrow (x - 3, y)$. Explain how to create this transformation and which of the three types it is.

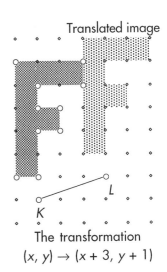

The transformation $(x, y) \rightarrow (x + 3, y + 1)$

2. Drag parts of your sketch until it demonstrates the transformation $(x, y) \rightarrow (-x, y)$. Explain how to create this transformation and which of the three types it is.

3. If you combine a translation with a reflection, you get a special two-step isometry called a **glide reflection.**

Step 1   In a new sketch, construct a triangle. Translate the triangle; then reflect its translated image.

Step 2   Hide the intermediate triangle so that only the first and last triangles are showing. The last triangle is the glide reflection image of the first.

Step 3   Now you will learn a shortcut for continuing your glide reflection. Select a vertex of the first triangle and the corresponding vertex of the image triangle and choose Define Transform in the Transform menu. Look over the information in the dialog box, and then click Define.

Step 4   Select the image triangle and choose 2 Step Transform in the Transform menu.

Step 5   Repeat your transformation on the newest image triangle a few more times.

a. Explain why it makes sense for the name of this transformation to contain both the word *glide* and the word *reflection*.

b. Explain how a set of footprints made by a person walking down a beach is an example of a glide reflection.

Lesson 8.2

Properties of Isometries

In this activity, you will demonstrate an important property of a reflection. Then you will investigate the transformations you can produce using two reflections.

Investigation 8.2.1: Poolroom Math

When you hit a pool ball without putting any spin on it, the ball follows a straight path toward the cushion. It bounces off the cushion at the same angle at which it came in. Can you see how this path is like a reflection?

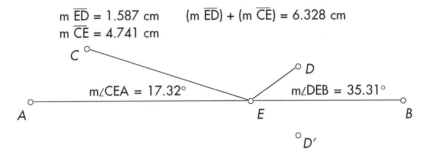

m $\overline{ED}$ = 1.587 cm   (m $\overline{ED}$) + (m $\overline{CE}$) = 6.328 cm
m $\overline{CE}$ = 4.741 cm

m∠CEA = 17.32°   m∠DEB = 35.31°

Sketch

Step 1   Construct a long horizontal segment *AB* to represent the cushion.

Step 2   Draw points *C* and *D* on the same side of the segment. Point *C* represents the cue ball, and point *D* represents the target ball you plan to hit.

Step 3   Construct $\overline{CE}$ and $\overline{ED}$, where point *E* is a point on $\overline{AB}$. These segments together show the path of the cue ball with one bounce off the cushion.

Step 4   Measure *CE* and *ED*.

Step 5   Use the calculator to find the sum of these two lengths.

Step 6   Measure the incoming and outgoing angles the cue ball makes with the cushion (angles *CEA* and *DEB*). To measure an angle, select three points on the angle in order, making sure that the vertex is the middle selection. Then choose Angle in the Measure menu.

Step 7   Double-click segment *AB* to mark it as a mirror. Then reflect point *D* across this segment to create point *D′*.

Investigate

1.   Drag point *E* and observe the angle measures. Locate point *E* at the point on the cushion where the cue ball should hit. Explain how you found this point.

2.   Construct $\overline{CD'}$ and change its line weight to dashed using the Display menu. Explain how you can use the reflection of point *D* to figure out how to aim the cue ball.

3.   Now drag point *E* again, this time watching the sum *CE + ED*. How is this total distance related to the correct path of the cue ball? (Note: If you set your calculation precision to thousandths using Preferences in the Display menu, you can observe this sum more precisely.)

4.   How can you use reflections to find the minimal path between two points if your path must visit a neighboring line? Write your observations as the Minimal Path Conjecture (C-75).

Investigation 8.2.3: Reflecting over Two Intersecting Lines

Sketch

Step 1   In a new sketch, construct any irregular polygon interior. Show one of its point's labels.

Step 2   Construct two intersecting lines, each with its own two control points. Construct the point of intersection.

Step 3   Mark the closest line as a mirror by double-clicking it; then reflect the polygon and the labeled point across this line. Change the shading or color of the image.

Step 4   Mark the other line as a mirror, and reflect the image from the first reflection across this second line. Change the shading or color of this second image.

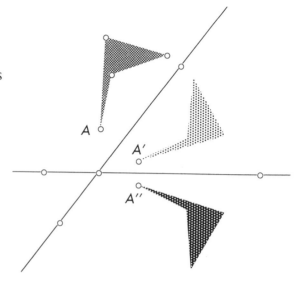

Investigate

5.   Now you will investigate a single isometry that transforms the original figure onto its second image. Construct $\overline{AI}$, where point A is a point on the original figure and point I is the point of intersection of the lines. Construct $\overline{IJ}$, where point J is a free point. Double-click point I to mark it as a center for rotation. Measure $\angle AIJ$; then, with the points still selected, choose Mark Angle in the Transform menu to mark $\angle AIJ$ as a rotation angle. Finally, use the Transform menu to rotate your original figure by the marked angle. Drag point J to move the rotated image around. Can you make the rotated image coincide with the second reflection image? What single isometry transforms the original figure to the second reflection image?

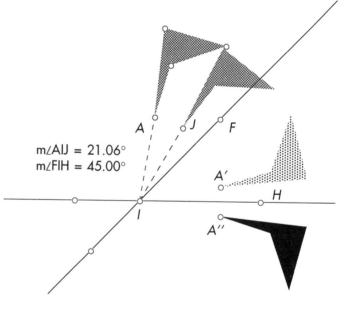

6.   Measure one of the smaller angles formed by the intersecting mirror lines. Drag point J so that it coincides with point A˝. Compare the two angle measures showing on your screen. How are they related?

7.   Collect all your observations about a figure reflected across two intersecting lines. Write them as a conjecture (C-77).

Investigation 8.2.2: Reflecting over Two Parallel Lines

Sketch

Step 5   Drag a point on one of the lines until the angle measurements disappear and the lines are parallel.

Step 6   Select the labeled point on the original (point *A* in the picture) and the corresponding point on the second reflection image, and choose Distance in the Measure menu.

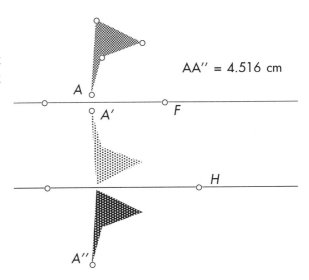

AA″ = 4.516 cm

Investigate

8.   To measure the distance between the two parallel lines, select one line and any point on the other line and choose Distance in the Measure menu. Drag a line, keeping them parallel. Describe the relationship between the two distance measures.

9.   Describe how you could transform the original polygon onto the second reflected image using only one transformation. (Try it yourself if you have time!)

10. Combine your observations about a figure reflected across one line and then across a second line parallel to the first. Write them as a single conjecture (C-76).

Explore More

1.   Rotate a figure by some arbitrary angle. Hide the center of rotation. Then locate two intersecting lines such that reflecting the figure across one and then the other results in the same image as the rotation. Then show the hidden center point and describe your results.

2.   Construct three lines that intersect in three points. Construct a polygon and reflect it across one of the lines. Reflect the image across a second line. Reflect this second image across the third line. Hide the two intermediate polygons. Select the original figure and the last image. Choose Define Transform in the Transform menu. Apply this three-step transformation to the image polygon, then to the new image, and so on, creating several images. What single isometry is equivalent to three reflections?

Lesson 8.3

Symmetry

A figure has **reflectional symmetry** if there is at least one line such that, if you reflect the figure across the line, the image will coincide with the original figure. The line you reflect across is called a **line of symmetry** or a **mirror line**. A figure has **rotational symmetry** if you can rotate some number of degrees about some point and get the same shape in the same position. In this exploration, you'll look for reflectional and rotational symmetries of regular polygons.

Investigation 8.3

Sketch

Step 1   Construct a regular polygon and its interior. (Construct it from scratch, or use a script.) You can use an equilateral triangle, a square, a regular pentagon, a regular hexagon, or any other regular polygon. You may want to divide these shapes among the different groups in your class.

Step 2   If the polygon's center doesn't already exist, construct it.

Step 3   Construct a line, and reflect your figure's interior across the line. Give the image a lighter shade.

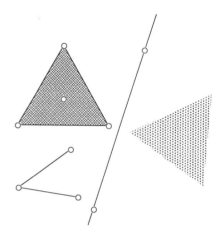

Investigate

1.   Drag the line until the image of your polygon coincides with the original. Describe how the line is positioned relative to the figure.

2.   When a reflection image coincides with the original figure, the reflection line is a line of symmetry. Drag the line so it is a different line of symmetry. Continue doing this until you have found all the different reflectional symmetries of your polygon. Record your total. (Note: Be careful not to count the same line twice!)

3.   To look for rotational symmetries, you will need to rotate your polygon. Double-click the center of the polygon to mark it as a center for rotation. Then construct an angle below your polygon, select the points that define it, and choose Mark Angle in the Transform menu. Also measure the angle. Rotate the figure by this marked angle. Finally, manipulate the angle so that the rotated image fits exactly over the original figure. What angle measure causes the figures to coincide?

4.   Continue changing your angle to find all possible rotational symmetries of your polygon. Consider angles greater than 180°, even though Sketchpad will measure them as less than 180°. Count the number of times the rotated image coincides with the original when rotating from more than 0° to 360°. Don't bother with rotations greater than 360°. Record the total number of rotational symmetries you found.

5.   Combine the results from other members of your class to describe the reflectional and rotational symmetries of other regular polygons. Complete a chart like the one below.

Number of sides of regular polygon	3	4	5	6	...	8	...	n
Number of reflectional symmetries	-?-	-?-	-?-	-?-	...	-?-	...	-?-
Number of rotational symmetries	-?-	-?-	-?-	-?-	...	-?-	...	-?-

6. Use your findings to make a conjecture about the reflectional and rotational symmetries of a regular *n*-gon. Include in your conjecture a statement about the smallest angle of rotational symmetry for a regular *n*-gon (C-78).

Explore More

1. Construct one of the regular polygons using rotations or some combination of rotations and reflections. Explain your method and how it takes advantage of the symmetry of the polygon.

2. Explore symmetries in other figures. For example, try rhombuses, rectangles, isosceles trapezoids, or kites.

Lesson 8.6

Tessellations Using Only Translations

In this activity, you'll learn how to construct an irregularly shaped tile based on a parallelogram. Then you'll use translations to tessellate your screen with this tile.

Sketch

Step 1   Construct $\overline{AB}$ in the lower left corner of your sketch, and construct point C just above $\overline{AB}$.

Step 2   Select point A, then point B, and mark this vector in the Transform menu.

Step 3   Select point C and translate it by the marked vector. (Use the Transform menu to do this.)

Step 4   Construct the remaining sides of your parallelogram.

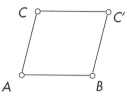

Steps 1–4

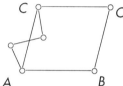  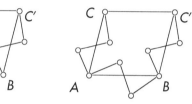 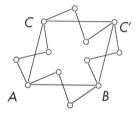

Step 5   Step 6   Step 7   Steps 8 and 9

Step 5   Construct two or three connected segments from point A to point C. We'll call this *irregular edge AC*.

Step 6   Select all the segments and points of irregular edge AC and translate them by the marked vector. (Vector AB should still be marked.)

Step 7   Now you will do the same to the other pair of parallel sides. Use segments to make an irregular edge from A to B.

Step 8   Mark the vector from A to C. (To do this, select points A and C in order and choose Mark Vector in the Transform menu.)

Step 9   Select all the parts of irregular edge AB and translate them by the marked vector.

Step 10 Select each of the vertices of your irregular edges in order around the figure, and choose Polygon Interior from the Construct menu. This is the tile you will translate.

Step 11 Select the polygon interior and translate it by the marked vector. (You probably still have vector *AC* marked.)

Step 12 Repeat this process until you have a column of tiles all the way up your sketch. Change the shading or color on every other tile to create a pattern.

Step 13 Mark vector *AB*. Then select all the polygon interiors in your column of tiles and translate them by this marked vector.

Step 14 Continue translating columns of tiles until you fill your screen. Select alternate tiles to create a pattern. Change shades and colors so you can see your tessellation.

Step 15 Drag vertices of your original tile until you get a shape that you like or that is recognizable as some interesting form.

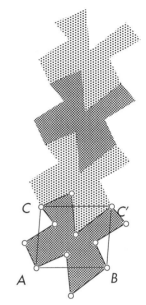

Steps 10–12

Explore More

1. Animate your tessellation. (Here's a simple way to do this: Construct a small circle near a point of your original tile. Select the point as well as the circle, and choose Animate in the Display menu.)

2. Use Sketchpad to make a translation tessellation that starts with a regular hexagon as the basic shape instead of a parallelogram. (Hint: The process is very similar; it just involves a third pair of sides.)

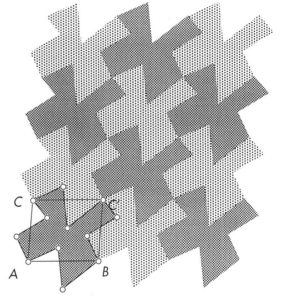

Steps 13 and 14

Lesson 8.7

Tessellations That Use Rotations

The translational tessellations in the last lesson have tiles that all face in the same direction. A tessellation that uses rotations has tiles facing in different directions. The designs in a rotational tessellation have rotational symmetry about points in the tiling.

Sketch

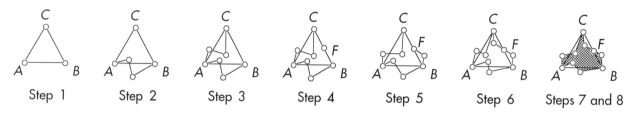

Step 1   Step 2   Step 3   Step 4   Step 5   Step 6   Steps 7 and 8

Step 1   Construct equilateral triangle *ABC* as shown in the picture. (You may already have an equilateral triangle tool. If you don't and you are having trouble figuring out how to construct an equilateral triangle, ask your teacher for hints.)

Step 2   Construct two or three connected segments from *A* to *B*. We'll call this *irregular edge AB*.

Step 3   Double-click point *A* to mark it as a center. Then select all the points and segments of irregular edge *AB* and rotate it by 60°. (You'll find Rotate in the Transform menu.)

Step 4   Construct midpoint *F* of side *CB*. (Select the segment and use the Construct menu.)

Step 5   Construct two connected segments from *B* to *F*. We'll call this *irregular edge BF*.

Step 6   Double-click point *F* to mark it as a center. Then select all the points and segments of irregular edge *BF* and rotate them by 180°.

Step 7   You have finished the edges of your tile. Drag points on the edges until none of the irregular edges intersect.

Step 8   Select each of the vertices of your irregular edges in order around the figure, and choose Polygon Interior from the Construct menu. This is the tile you will tessellate with.

Step 9   To construct a new tile, mark point *A*, point *B*, point *C*, or point *F* as a center for rotation and rotate the polygon interior by an appropriate number of degrees. Change the color or shading of your new tile so you can see it more clearly.

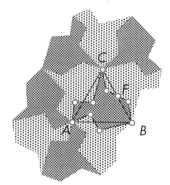

Step 10   Continue this process until you have tiled a section of your sketch with at least ten tiles. Be patient, and remember to use Undo in the Edit menu when you make a mistake!

Step 11   Drag vertices of your original tile until you get a shape that you like or that is recognizable as some interesting form.

Explore More

1.   Use the directions on page 413 in *Discovering Geometry* to make a tessellation based on a regular hexagon.

2.   Use the directions on page 417 in *Discovering Geometry* to make a tessellation based on a parallelogram.

Area

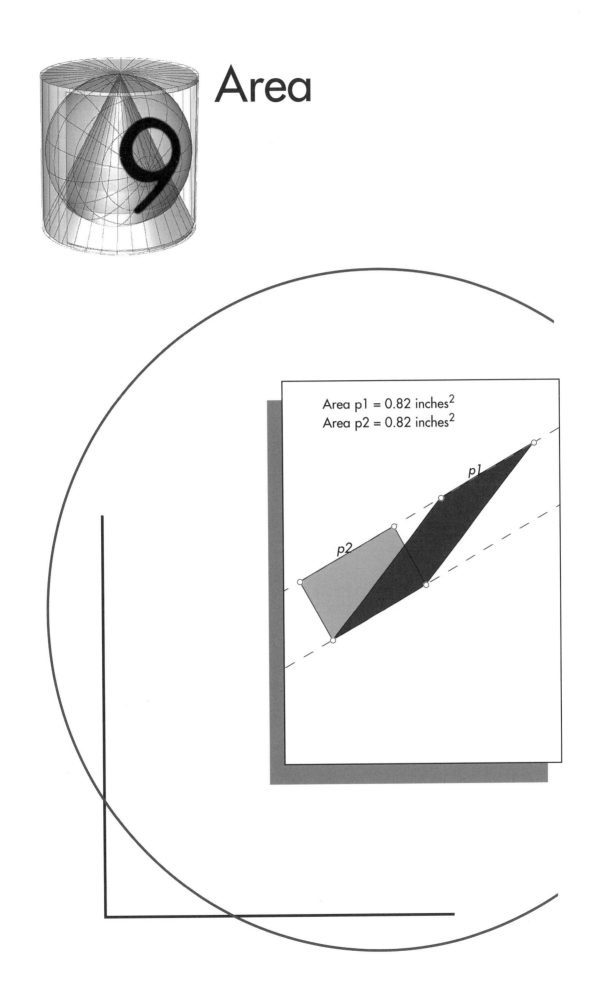

Area p1 = 0.82 inches^2
Area p2 = 0.82 inches^2

p1

p2

Lesson 9.1

Areas of Rectangles and Parallelograms

The method for finding the area of a rectangle is probably familiar to you. In this lesson, you'll review that method and use it to derive a method for finding the area of a parallelogram.

Investigation 9.1.1

Sketch

In steps 1–6, you'll construct a rectangle with a line through one side.

Step 1   Construct a horizontal segment AB.

Step 2   Construct lines perpendicular to $\overline{AB}$ through points A and B.

Step 3   Construct point C on the vertical line through A.

Step 4   Construct a line through point C parallel to $\overline{AB}$.

Step 5   Construct point D where this line intersects the vertical line through point B.

Step 6   Hide the two vertical lines, and construct segments AC and BD to complete your rectangle.

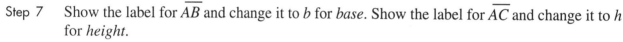

Steps 1–7

Step 7   Show the label for $\overline{AB}$ and change it to b for *base*. Show the label for $\overline{AC}$ and change it to h for *height*.

Step 8   Measure the lengths b and h.

Step 9   If these lengths are not displayed in centimeters, choose Preferences in the Display menu and choose cm for the distance unit.

Investigate

1. Use the calculator to create an expression in terms of b and h that you think gives the area of the rectangle. To confirm that your expression is correct, you can look at your rectangle on a grid. Choose Show Grid in the Measure menu. Drag points A and B so that they snap to points on the grid, keeping $\overline{AB}$ horizontal. The length b should be a whole number. Drag point C so that the top line passes through grid points. Point C won't snap to the grid, but h should be close to a whole number. If the

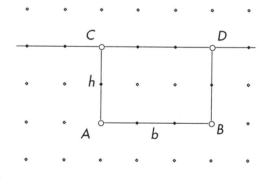

expression you calculated is correct, it should be close to a whole number of square units. Count the number of square units in the rectangle. Is your expression correct? If not, see if you can correct it. Once the expression is correct, drag your rectangle to make sure that your expression works for any rectangle. Write a formula that gives the area of a rectangle where A is the area, b is the length of the base, and h is the height of the rectangle (C-81: Rectangle Area Conjecture).

Investigation 9.1.2

Sketch

Now you'll construct a parallelogram with the same base and height as the rectangle.

Step 10 Continuing in the same sketch, construct $\overline{AG}$, where point G is a point on the line through the top of the rectangle.

Step 11 Construct a line through point B parallel to $\overline{AG}$.

Step 12 Construct point H where the line intersects $\overleftrightarrow{CD}$.

Step 13 Hide $\overleftrightarrow{BH}$ and construct $\overline{BH}$.

Step 14 Measure AG and BH.

Step 15 Construct polygon interior $AGHB$.

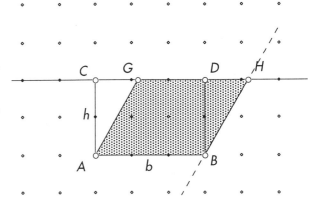

Investigate

Drag point G and answer the following questions.

2. As you move point G, what side lengths change?

3. What measures in your sketch stay the same as you move point G?

4. In this construction, is the height h of the rectangle the same as the height of the parallelogram?

5. Is it possible to drag point G so that the parallelogram fills in the rectangle?

6. Without measuring the area of the parallelogram, do you think its area changes when you drag point G? After you have made your prediction, measure the area of the polygon interior to check it. Write down your observation.

7. Write a formula for the area of a parallelogram (C-82: Parallelogram Area Conjecture).

Explore More

In the figure above, what do you notice about $\triangle ACG$ and $\triangle BDH$? Draw a parallelogram on a piece of paper. Cut it out and then show how you can cut it into two pieces that can be arranged to form a rectangle. Explain how this demonstrates the Parallelogram Area Conjecture.

Lesson 9.2

Areas of Triangles, Trapezoids, and Kites

In this lesson, you will discover formulas for the areas of triangles, trapezoids, and kites.

Investigation 9.2.1: Area of Triangles

Sketch

Step 1   Choose Preferences in the Display menu to make sure that the distance unit is centimeters.

Step 2   In the Graph menu, choose Show Grid. Then choose Hide Axes.

Step 3   Construct $\triangle CDE$.

Step 4   Construct the midpoint F of $\overline{DE}$.

Step 5   Double-click on point F to mark it as a center for rotation.

Step 6   Select point C, $\overline{CE}$, and $\overline{CD}$, and choose Rotate in the Transform menu. Rotate by a fixed angle of 180°.

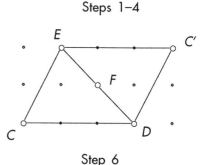

Steps 1–4

Step 6

Investigate

1.   Drag the vertices of your original triangle. What kind of quadrilateral is $CDC'E$ no matter what shape $\triangle CDE$ is?

2.   What is the formula for the area of quadrilateral $CDC'E$ in terms of b and h?

3.   What is the area of $\triangle CDE$ compared to the area of the entire quadrilateral?

4.   Write your findings as a conjecture (C-83: Triangle Area Conjecture).

Investigation 9.2.2: Area of Trapezoids

Sketch

Step 1   In a new sketch, choose Show Grid in the Graph menu. Then choose Hide Axes.

Step 2   Construct $\overline{CD}$.

Step 3   Construct point E and a line through point E parallel to $\overline{CD}$.

Step 4   Construct point F on the line.

Step 5   Hide $\overleftrightarrow{EF}$.

Step 6   Construct $\overline{CE}$, $\overline{EF}$, and $\overline{FD}$ to complete trapezoid $CEFD$.

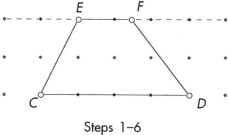

Steps 1–6

Step 7   Show the labels of $\overline{EF}$ and $\overline{CD}$ and change them to b_1 and b_2.

Investigate

5.   Construct the midpoint of one of the nonparallel sides and rotate the trapezoid 180° around this midpoint. What kind of shape do you have?

6.   What's the length of the base of this doubled trapezoid?

7.   Based on your observations, write a formula for the area A of a trapezoid using b_1 for one base, b_2 for the second base, and h for the height. Write your findings as a conjecture (C-84: Trapezoid Area Conjecture).

Investigation 9.2.3: Area of Kites

Sketch

Step 1   In a new sketch, choose Show Grid in the Graph menu. Then choose Hide Axes.

Step 2   Construct $\overline{CD}$. This will be one diagonal of your kite.

Step 3   Double-click $\overline{CD}$ to mark it as a mirror for a reflection.

Step 4   Construct point E. While it's selected, choose Reflect in the Transform menu to construct point E'

Step 5   Construct $\overline{ED}$, $\overline{DE'}$, $\overline{E'C}$, and $\overline{CE}$ to complete kite $CEDE'$.

Step 6   Construct $\overline{EE'}$, the other diagonal of the kite.

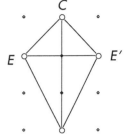

Investigate

8. Recall some of the properties of a kite. The diagonal connecting the vertex angles of the kite divides the kite into two congruent triangles. It is also the perpendicular bisector of the other diagonal. Can you calculate the area of a kite if you know the lengths of the two diagonals? Write a formula and use Sketchpad to test it. Write your findings as a conjecture (C-85: Kite Area Conjecture).

Explore More

1. Construct a triangle or a trapezoid whose perimeter you can change without changing the area.

2. Is there a formula that can be used to find the area of any quadrilateral? Design an investigation to explore this question.

Lesson 9.4

Areas of Regular Polygons

In this lesson, you will use Sketchpad to discover a formula for the area of a regular polygon. Recall that a regular polygon is equilateral and equiangular.

Investigation 9.4

Sketch

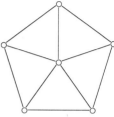

Step 1   Set a Script tool folder that has scripts for regular polygons in it. To set a Script tool folder, choose Preferences in the Display menu and click More. In the Advanced Preferences dialog, under Set Script Tool Folder, click Set. (You may first have to click Clear.) Navigate in the pop-up menu to find the desired folder. Click the Set button. Click Continue and then click OK to dismiss the Preferences dialog.

Step 2   Use a Script tool to construct a regular pentagon.

Steps 1–5

Step 3   Delete the polygon interior.

Step 4   Construct the pentagon's center if it doesn't already have one.

Step 5   Draw segments that connect the vertices to the center.

Investigate

1.   How many triangles did you form in the construction?

2.   Are the triangles congruent? Explain.

3.   What is the formula in terms of b and h for the area of one of the triangles?

4.   The **apothem** of a regular polygon is a perpendicular segment from the center of the polygon to a side of the polygon. This segment is also the altitude of each of the congruent triangles that form the polygon. Write the formula for the area of one of the triangles of your pentagon in terms of the apothem a and the length of a side s.

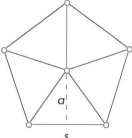

5.   Use your results from question 4 to write a formula for the area of the entire pentagon in terms of the apothem a and the length of a side s.

6.   Use your script tools to construct other regular polygons. How many congruent triangles can you make by connecting the vertices to the center of a regular polygon with n sides?

7.   Write a formula for the area of any regular n-gon where A is the area, a is the apothem, s is the length of one side, and n is the number of sides.

8.   Let p be the perimeter of a regular n-gon. Rewrite the formula in question 7, substituting p for part of the formula (C-86: Regular Polygon Area Conjecture).

Explore More

Construct an apothem in a regular polygon. Make measurements and use the calculator to create an expression that gives the area of the polygon. Construct the polygon interior and measure its area to confirm that the expression you created works.

Lesson 9.5

Areas of Circles

The formula for the area of a circle can be derived from the formula for the area of a regular polygon. In this activity, you will experiment with a sketch that demonstrates this.

Investigation 9.5

Sketch

Step 1   Open the sketch To a Circle (Mac) or ch09\polycirc.gsp (Windows).

Step 2   Drag or animate the point *drag* along the segment. To animate, double-click the animate button.

Investigate

1. What do you observe about the area of the inscribed regular polygon compared to the area of the circle as the number of sides of the polygon increases?

2. What is the formula for the circumference *C* of the circle in terms of *r*?

3. What is the formula for the area of the inscribed polygon in terms of *a* (apothem) and *p* (perimeter)?

4. As the number of sides of the regular polygon increases, the apothem becomes close to the radius, and the perimeter of the polygon approaches the circumference of the circle. In the formula you wrote for question 3, substitute *C* for *p* and *r* for *a*.

5. Simplify your answer to question 4 to write a formula for the area *A* of a circle with radius *r* (C-87: Circle Area Conjecture).

Explore More

Use Sketchpad to construct the figure shown on the right. What is the ratio of the area of the circle to the area of the square? Use algebra to explain your results.

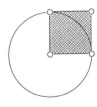

Pythagorean Theorem

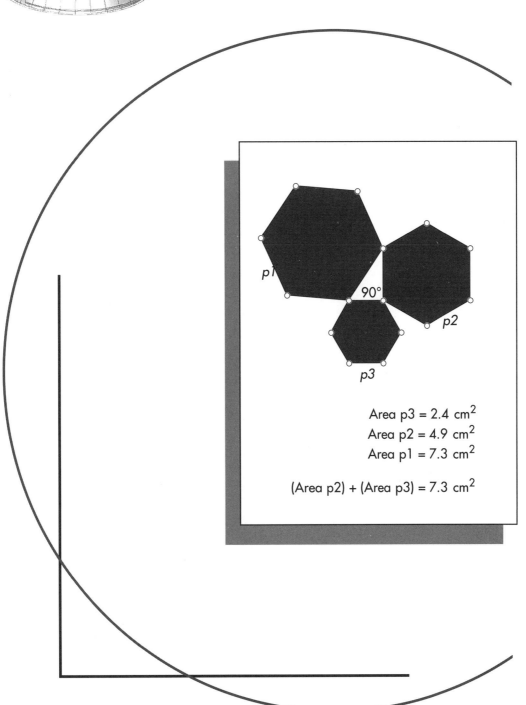

Area p3 = 2.4 cm^2
Area p2 = 4.9 cm^2
Area p1 = 7.3 cm^2

(Area p2) + (Area p3) = 7.3 cm^2

Lesson 10.1

The Theorem of Pythagoras

The Pythagorean Theorem states a relationship among the areas of squares constructed on the three sides of a right triangle. In this investigation, you'll explore this relationship in two ways: first by measuring and calculating, and second by cutting the squares on the two legs of the right triangle and arranging them to fit in the square on the hypotenuse.

Investigation 10.1

Sketch

Step 1   Construct $\overline{AB}$.

Step 2   Construct the midpoint C of $\overline{AB}$.

Step 3   Construct a circle centered at C with radius endpoint B.

Step 4   Construct $\overline{AD}$ and $\overline{BD}$, where point D is a point on the circle.

Step 5   Hide the circle and the midpoint. Drag points A, B, and D to be sure your triangle stays a right triangle.

Step 6   Set a Script tool folder that has a script in it for a square. This can be either a folder of tools you have made yourself or the regular polygons folder that came with Sketchpad and with this book. To set a Script tool folder, choose Preferences in the Display menu and click More. In the Advanced Preferences dialog under Set Script Tool Folder, click Set. (You may first have to click Clear.) Navigate in the pop-up menu to find the desired folder. Click the Set button. Click Continue; then click OK to dismiss the Preferences dialog.

Step 7   Construct squares on the sides of the triangle using the Script tool square.

Step 8   Measure the areas of the three squares.

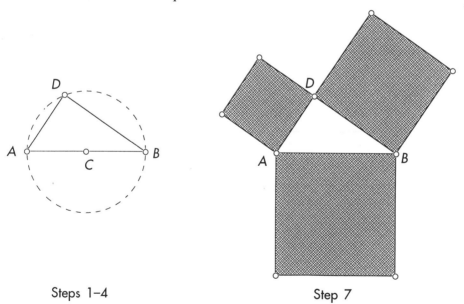

Steps 1–4   Step 7

Investigate

1. Drag vertices of the triangle and look for a relationship among the areas of the three squares. Use the calculator to confirm your observation. State a conjecture about these three areas.

2. The Pythagorean Theorem is most often stated as an equation with variables representing side lengths. Before you state the theorem in this way, you need to recall how to express the area of a square. What is the area of a square with side length a?

3. Complete the following statement: In a right triangle, if a and b are the lengths of the legs and c is the length of the hypotenuse, then –?– (C-88: Pythagorean Theorem).

Sketch

You can use dissection puzzles to demonstrate that figures have equal areas without measuring them. Continue in your sketch to create a dissection that demonstrates the Pythagorean Theorem.

Step 9 Delete the square interiors on the longer leg and on the hypotenuse, but not on the smaller leg.

Step 10 Find point O, the center of the square on the longer leg, by constructing the diagonals.

Step 11 Hide the diagonals.

Step 12 Construct a line through point O parallel to hypotenuse AB.

Step 13 Construct a line through point O perpendicular to hypotenuse AB.

Step 14 Construct the four points where these two new lines intersect the sides of the square.

Step 15 Construct the polygon interiors of the four quadrilaterals in the larger square.

Step 16 Hide the lines.

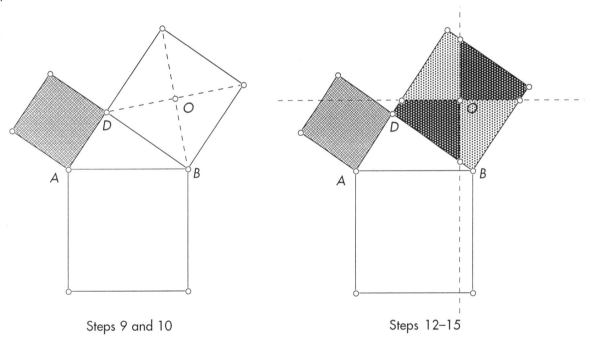

Steps 9 and 10   Steps 12–15

Investigate

4. You should now have a five-piece puzzle. One piece is the square on the small leg, and four pieces form the square on the longer leg. The object of the puzzle is to arrange these five pieces to fit in the square on the hypotenuse. Hold down the Shift key and click on each of the five interiors to select them all. Choose Cut in the Edit menu; then choose Paste. Your five pieces are now free to be moved. Click in a blank area of your sketch to deselect everything, and then drag each piece and find a way to fit all the pieces in the square on the hypotenuse. When you finish, draw the solution on your paper. (That is, draw a square and sketch how the five pieces fit into the square.)

5. Explain how this dissection demonstrates the Pythagorean Theorem.

Lesson 10.2

Is the Converse True?

To investigate the converse of the Pythagorean Theorem, you can construct squares on the sides of an ordinary triangle and then manipulate the triangle until the squares satisfy the theorem.

Sketch

Step 1   Construct a triangle ABC. It should not be a right triangle.

Step 2   Construct squares and their interiors on the three sides of the triangle. Use a script such as 4/Square (By Edge) (Mac) or regpoly\4byedge.gss (Windows).

Step 3   Measure the areas of the three squares.

Step 4   Calculate the sum of the two smaller areas.

Area BAFG = 1.319 cm^2
Area CBDE = 2.912 cm^2
Area ACHI = 5.098 cm^2
(Area BAFG) + (Area CBDE) = 4.231 cm^2

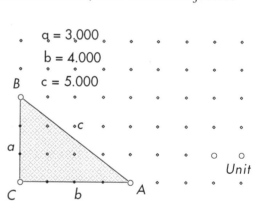

Investigate

1.   Drag a vertex of the triangle and make the sum you calculated approximately equal to the area of the third square. Once you've done this, your triangle's side lengths satisfy the Pythagorean Theorem. What kind of triangle do you have? Measure an angle to confirm your observation; then write a conjecture (C-89: Converse of the Pythagorean Theorem).

2.   Open the sketch Triple Checker (Mac) or ch10\triplchk.gsp (Windows). A set of three positive integers that satisfies the Pythagorean formula is called a **Pythagorean triple**. One such set is 3-4-5, because $3^2 + 4^2 = 5^2$. Below are a few more sets of three numbers. To find out which sets are and which sets are not Pythagorean triples, drag the triangle and try to match side lengths with the numbers in each set. (Drag the point *Unit* to scale the grid.) For each set that is not a Pythagorean triple, write an inequality that shows that those numbers do not work in the Pythagorean formula. Record any other triples you find that are not in this list.

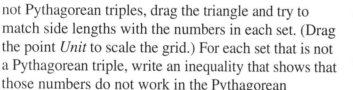

a. 6-8-10   b. 5-12-13   c. 8-15-17   d. 7-24-25   e. 9-12-17

Lesson 10.4

Two Special Right Triangles

In this lesson, you'll discover shortcuts that will enable you to find side lengths quickly in two types of special right triangles. The first special triangle you'll investigate is half a square. Then you'll investigate the right triangle that is half an equilateral triangle.

Investigation 10.4.2

Sketch

Step 1   Construct a square *ABCD*. (Use a Script tool.)

Step 2   Construct diagonal *CA*.

Step 3   Hide the square's interior, if it has one.

Step 4   Change the line weights of $\overline{CD}$ and $\overline{DA}$ to dashed.

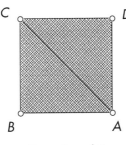
Steps 1 and 2

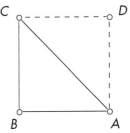
Steps 3 and 4

Step 5   Use the square script to construct squares on the sides of right triangle *ABC*.

Step 6   Construct one diagonal in each of the smaller squares as shown at right.

Investigate

1. Triangle *ABC* in the figure at right is an isosceles right triangle. Without measuring, figure out the measure of each angle in an isosceles right triangle.

2. The diagonals you drew in the smaller squares may help you see a relationship between the smaller squares and the square on the hypotenuse. If each of the smaller squares has area x^2, what is the area of the large square? Confirm your conjecture by measuring the areas. Drag the triangle to confirm that this relationship is always true.

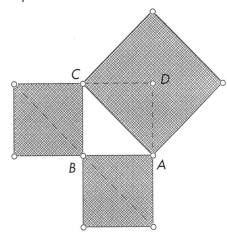
Steps 5 and 6

3. Copy and complete this conjecture: In an isosceles right triangle, if the legs have length *x*, then the hypotenuse has length –?– (C-90: Isosceles Right Triangle Conjecture).

Investigation 10.4.3

Sketch

Step 1   In a new sketch, construct an equilateral triangle *ABC*. Use a Script tool or construct it from scratch.

Step 2   Construct the midpoint *D* of $\overline{AB}$ and construct median *CD*.

Step 3   Hide the triangle's interior, if necessary.

Step 4   Change the line weights of $\overline{AB}$ and $\overline{AC}$ to dashed.

Step 5   Construct $\overline{BD}$ and make its line weight thin.

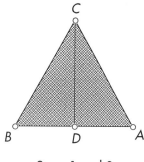

Steps 1 and 2

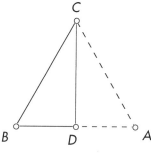

Steps 3–5

Investigate

4.   Without measuring, figure out the measure of each angle in $\triangle BCD$.

5.   In a 30-60 right triangle, how does the length of the hypotenuse compare to the length of the shortest leg? Write a conjecture (C-91).

6.   Construct squares on the three sides of the 30-60 right triangle as shown at right. If the smallest square has area x^2, what is the area of the square on the hypotenuse?

7.   Using your answer to question 6 and the Pythagorean Theorem, write an expression for the area of the square on the longer leg.

8.   Copy and complete this conjecture: In a 30-60 right triangle, if the shorter leg has length *x*, then the longer leg has length –?– and the hypotenuse has length –?– (C-92: 30-60 Right Triangle Conjecture).

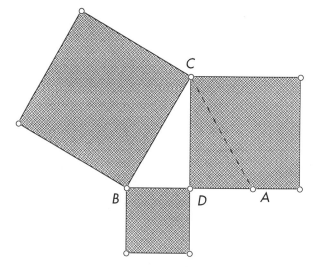

Lesson 10.5

Multiples of Right Triangles

Being able to recognize Pythagorean triples can help you solve some problems quickly. In this lesson, you'll discover how you can generate many Pythagorean triples from just a few.

Investigation 10.5.1

Sketch

Step 1   Open the sketch Triple Check (Mac) or ch10\triplchk.gsp (Windows). In that sketch, you'll see a right triangle with side lengths 3, 4, and 5 drawn on the grid. (To scale the grid, drag the point labeled *Unit*.)

Step 2   Double-click point *C* to mark it as a center for dilation.

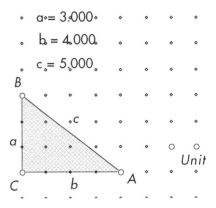

Investigate

1. Drag point *B* to add one unit to length *a*; then drag point *A* to add one unit to length *b*. Is *c* still an integer?

2. Keep adding equal amounts to both *a* and *b* and note whether *c* is ever an integer. If you add the same amount to leg lengths in a Pythagorean triple, is the hypotenuse length still an integer?

3. Make the triangle a 3-4-5 right triangle again. This time you'll change the triangle using the Dilation tool. To choose the Dilation tool, press and hold the mouse button down on the Selection Arrow tool; then drag to the tool at the far right. Select the entire triangle, including all three vertices. Drag point *A* to the right. The Dilation tool stretches the triangle, but not by adding the same amount to each leg. Keep dragging until you get another Pythagorean triple (all three side lengths must be integers). Record this triple. Keep enlarging the triangle, and record at least two more triples.

4. Choose the first Selection Arrow tool (the Translate tool). Make the unit a little bit smaller so that you can make a small 5-12-13 right triangle. Now choose the Dilation tool again and enlarge your triangle to find another triple. Record this triple and also record the next triple you think you would get if you kept enlarging.

5. Consider the triple 8-15-17. Show that if you double each number, the resulting set of numbers still works in the Pythagorean formula.

6. The set of numbers 14-48-50 is a Pythagorean triple. What smaller triple is it a multiple of?

7. If three numbers are the lengths of the sides of a right triangle, how can you easily find another set of lengths that are also sides of a right triangle? Write your conclusion as the Pythagorean Multiples Conjecture (C-93).

Lesson 10.7

Distance in Coordinate Geometry

You can use the Pythagorean Theorem to derive a formula to find the distance between any two points in a coordinate plane. The Distance Formula can in turn be used to derive the equation for a circle.

Investigation 10.7

Sketch

Open the sketch Coordinate Distance (Mac) or ch10\distance.gsp (Windows).

Investigate

The object in questions 1–5 is to look for relationships among the measures and calculations in the sketch to derive a formula that gives the distance between two points in a plane. Resist playing with the action buttons for the moment.

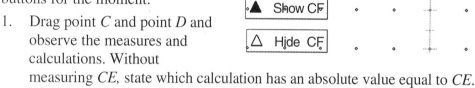

C: (1.00, 1.00)
E: (4.00, 1.00)
D: (4.00, 3.00)

$x_D - x_C = 3.00$
$y_D - y_C = 2.00$
CD = 3.61 cm

Show CF

Hide CF

1. Drag point C and point D and observe the measures and calculations. Without measuring CE, state which calculation has an absolute value equal to CE.

2. Which calculation has an absolute value equal to DE?

3. Use the Pythagorean Theorem to write an expression relating CD, CE, and DE.

4. In the sketch, use the calculator to create an expression using $x_D - x_C$ and $y_D - y_C$ that is equal to CD. (Hints: Use the ^ button for exponents. The square root function can be found in the Functions menu on the calculator. Don't forget to use parentheses where they're needed.) Once you've found the correct expression, write it down.

5. To generalize what you did in question 4, suppose the coordinates of two points A and B are (x_1, y_1) and (x_2, y_2), respectively. Write equations for AB^2 and for AB (C-95: Distance Formula).

6. Now you can play with the action buttons. Double-click the Show CF button. Point F represents all points (x, y) such that $CF = CD$. Drag point F and describe the locus it traces.

7. Construct a circle centered at point C using either point D or point F as a radius endpoint. Measure the equation of the circle. Drag point C or point D and look for relationships between the circle's equation and the coordinates of point C and the radius CD. Complete the following conjecture: The equation for a circle with radius r and center (h, k) is $(x - ?)^2 + (y - ?)^2 = (?)^2$ (C-96: Equation of a Circle).

8. Play a game with a partner to practice finding equations of a circle. To play, draw several circles in a sketch. Make sure no labels are showing. Measure the circles' equations. Have your partner match equations with circles. Drag a circle to check the matched equation. If the equation changes when the circle moves, then the match is correct.

Similarity

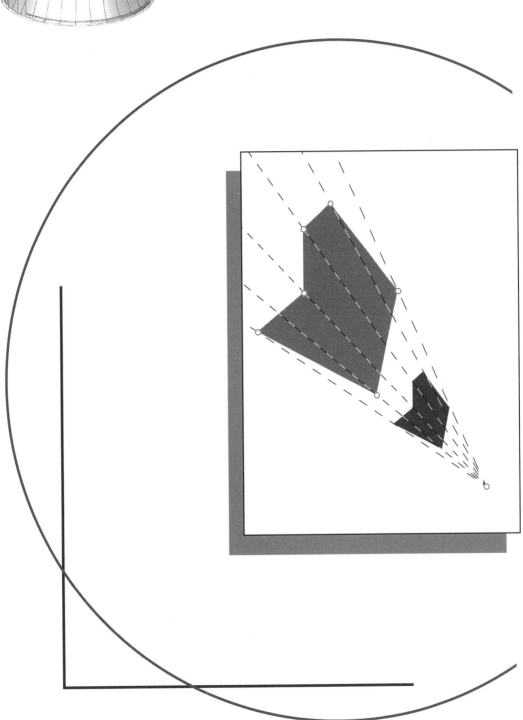

Lesson 12.2

Similarity

Figures are **similar** if they look the same. Similar figures have the same shape but not necessarily the same size. In this investigation, you'll use the Dilate command in the Transform menu to discover principles of **similarity**. You'll use your discoveries to come up with a definition of **similar polygons**.

Investigation: Similar Polygons

Sketch

Step 1   Construct any polygon.

Step 2   Construct a point outside the polygon and double-click to mark it as a center for dilation.

Step 3   Construct two segments of different lengths. Select them both and choose Mark Ratio in the Transform menu.

Step 4   Select your entire polygon and dilate by the marked ratio.

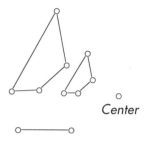

Center

Investigate

Now you can compare your two similar figures.

1. First drag the center of dilation. Also change the lengths of your two segments that define the ratio. Observe how this changes the similar polygons. How can you make the dilated image coincide with the original figure?

2. Change one of the ratio segments so that the dilated image is smaller than the original figure and doesn't intersect it. Select the dilated image and rotate it by any angle (45° is fine). This rotated image is congruent to the dilated image and is also similar to the original image. Experiment with the ratio segments again. Is it possible for similar figures to be congruent?

3. Measure the ratio of the segments you marked as ratio. Measure the ratios of some corresponding sides of your polygons. How do these ratios compare?

4. Measure some corresponding angles in these figures. How do these angles compare?

5. Write a definition of similar polygons.

6. Copy and complete this conjecture: If one polygon is the image of another polygon under a dilation, then –?– (C-101: Dilation Similarity Conjecture).

Explore More

1. To learn more about what a dilation does, construct rays from the point marked as the center through each vertex of your original polygon.

    a. What other point does each ray pass through?

    b. How does the distance between the center and the first polygon compare to the distance between the center and the second polygon?

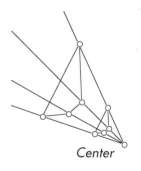

Center

2. Construct a pair of similar triangles without the Dilate command. Explain your method.

3. Construct two nonsimilar polygons whose corresponding angles are congruent. Explain your method.

4. Construct two nonsimilar polygons whose corresponding sides are proportional but whose corresponding angles are not congruent. Explain your method.

Lesson 12.3

Similar Triangles

In Chapter 5, you found shortcuts for determining whether two triangles are congruent. In this activity, you will find some shortcuts for determining whether two triangles are similar. It's not always convenient to check all three pairs of angles for congruence and all three pairs of sides for proportionality. It's handy to know which smaller sets of corresponding parts you can check instead.

Investigation: Finding Similarity Conjectures

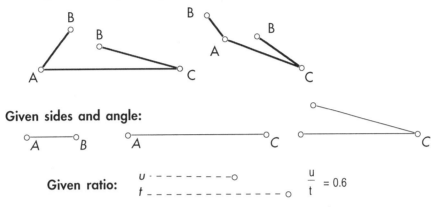

A sketch for investigating the possibility of an SSA similarity conjecture

You will check four different possible similarity conjectures using four different prepared sketches. You may want to divide up the four sketches among different groups around the room depending on how much time you have. The names of the sketches are:

AAA Similarity (Mac) or AAA_sim.gsp (Windows)

SSS Similarity (Mac) or SSS_sim.gsp (Windows)

SSA Similarity (Mac) or SSA_sim.gsp (Windows)

SAS Similarity (Mac) or SAS_sim.gsp (Windows)

Sketch

Open up one of the prepared sketches from the list above.

Investigate

1. Drag the vertices of the givens and observe how they affect the triangles (or fractured triangles) in your sketch.

    a. If your givens include any angles, explain the connection between the given angle(s) and the triangles (or fractured triangles) above.

    b. If your givens include any sides, explain the connection between the given side(s) and the triangles (or fractured triangles) above.

    c. If your givens include a ratio, explain the connection between the given ratio and the triangles (or fractured triangles) above.

2. If any triangles above the givens are fractured, drag parts of your sketch until you have two complete triangles. Do the triangles appear to be similar triangles?

3. To check for similarity, measure pairs of corresponding angles and ratios of corresponding sides. (To measure the ratio, select the shorter of the corresponding sides, then the longer, and choose Ratio in the Measure menu.) Use your measurements to describe whether your triangles are similar.

4. If you have already managed to create a pair of nonsimilar triangles, go right on to question 5. Otherwise, you need to continue your search for a counterexample. Change your givens to try at least one more case. Do your best to create a pair of nonsimilar triangles with the given constraints. Record your results.

5. If you are quite sure you can't find a counterexample, you have discovered a similarity shortcut. Record your results as a conjecture (C-102, C-103, or C-104). If you have found a counterexample, draw a sketch of the counterexample and explain why your similarity shortcut doesn't work.

6. Make sure you collect and record all the similarity conjectures. To do this, you may need to test some of the sample sketches yourself or gather information collected by your classmates.

Explore More

1. Construct a pair of triangles that are constrained by the requirements of one of the similarity shortcuts. Then demonstrate that these triangles are always similar. Explain your procedure in writing, or save a clearly captioned sketch containing your construction.

2. Explain why it is not necessary to check for an AAS similarity shortcut or an ASA similarity shortcut.

Lesson 12.4

Indirect Measurement with Similar Triangles

You can use similar triangles to calculate the heights of objects you are unable to measure directly. You can find the height of a tall object outdoors by measuring shadows on a sunny day. In Explore More, you will learn a different method for finding the height of a tall object that works even when it's cloudy.

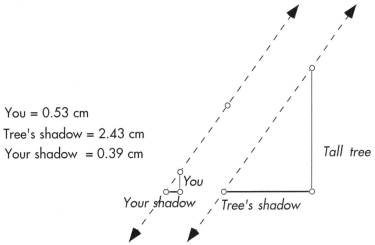

You = 0.53 cm
Tree's shadow = 2.43 cm
Your shadow = 0.39 cm

Investigation: Finding the Height of a Tall Tree Using Shadows

Sketch

Follow these steps to model this problem with a sketch similar to the one above.

Step 1   Draw a horizontal line. This will represent the ground.

Step 2   Construct two free points on the line. These will represent the places where your feet and the roots of the tree each meet the ground.

Step 3   Select both points and the line, and choose Perpendicular in the Construct menu.

Step 4   Use these perpendicular lines to construct segments that start at the ground and are perpendicular to the ground. Hide the lines.

Step 5   Label the two perpendicular segments. Change the labels so one segment is named after you and the other is called *Tall tree*. Adjust the heights so that the tree is much taller than you.

Step 6   Construct a diagonal attached to the point at the top of your head. Use the Display menu to change this line weight to dashed. This line represents the sun's ray as it makes a shadow on the ground.

Step 7   Since the sun is so far away, its rays are essentially parallel. Construct a segment parallel to the dashed line that passes through the top of the tree. (To do this, select the point and the dashed line and choose Parallel Line in the Construct menu.)

Step 8   Construct the points where both dashed lines intersect the ground. Now hide the line that represents the ground and construct segments to represent the shadows of both you and the tree.

Step 9   Change the weight of these shadows to thick. Also label the shadows after their objects.

Step 10 Since in reality the tree is very tall, you cannot measure its height. However, you can measure the length of the shadows and your own height. Measure these three lengths in your model sketch.

Investigate

1. Explain why the two triangles formed by you, the tree, and the two shadows are similar triangles.

2. Your model drawing is obviously a scale drawing. (You are actually much taller than the segment on your screen!) Drag the segment that represents you on your screen until its length represents your height in some way. For example, in the sketch above, the person is 53 inches tall, so she chose a segment that is 0.53 centimeter long. Drag your tree to a good height and slant the sun's rays to a reasonable angle. Now you can figure out the height of the tree. Using *only the three measurements you have already made,* figure out the height of the tree. Show and explain all your work.

3. Since this is only a model, you can check your reasoning in question 2 by measuring the height of the tree. Find this length. How well do your calculations match this measurement?

4. Suppose you measured the shadows of two straight objects at different times of day. Is it possible for the objects and their shadows to create similar triangles?

Explore More

Example B on page 603 in *Discovering Geometry* describes another method for finding the height of a tall object. This method doesn't require shadows. Construct a drawing that models this method. (Hint: Since the method involves reflection in a mirror, your sketch will require a reflection, too.)

Lesson 12.5

Corresponding Parts of Similar Triangles

You know that each pair of corresponding angles in a pair of similar triangles are congruent. You also know that each pair of corresponding sides are proportional. What about other corresponding parts of triangles, such as altitudes, medians, and angle bisectors?

Before you investigate this question, follow these steps to construct a pair of similar triangles.

Investigation 12.5.1

Sketch: Similar Triangles and Corresponding Altitudes

In steps 1–7, you'll construct a pair of similar triangles.

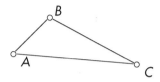 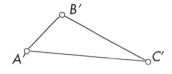

Steps 1 and 2: A pair of congruent triangles

Step 1   Construct any triangle *ABC*.

Step 2   First you will construct a triangle congruent to *ABC*. To do this, select the entire triangle and translate it by a reasonable distance and angle to keep it on your screen. (For example, an angle of 0° and a distance of roughly 3 inches or 10 centimeters might be reasonable, depending on your screen size.)

You have created triangle *A´B´C´*. Drag vertices of your original triangle and observe its translated image.

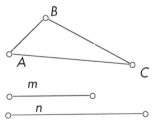 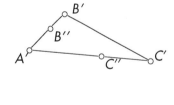

 $\dfrac{m}{n} = 0.6$

Steps 3–6: Dilating points on the second triangle

Step 3   Now you will dilate your second triangle so you can scale it to different sizes. First you need a ratio of dilation. Construct two horizontal segments *m* and *n*. Make *n* longer than *m*.

Step 4   First select *m*, then *n*, and choose Mark Ratio in the Transform menu. Then, with both segments still selected, choose Ratio in the Measure menu.

Step 5   Double-click *A´* in the second triangle to mark it as a center.

Step 6   Select *B´* and *C´* and dilate them by the marked ratio. These new points, *B´´* and *C´´*, are new vertices of your second triangle.

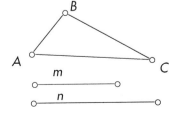 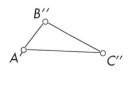

 $\dfrac{m}{n} = 0.7$

Step 7: Finishing the similar triangles

Step 7 To finish constructing triangle *A'B''C''*, hide points *B'* and *C'* and segments *A'B'* and *A'C'* and complete the missing segments of the new triangle. Change your ratio and observe the results.

Sketch

In steps 8–10, you'll construct altitudes and measure their ratio.

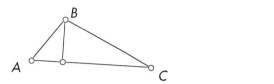

Steps 8 and 9: Constructing the altitudes

Step 8 Select a vertex and the side opposite that vertex and choose Perpendicular in the Construct menu. This gives you a whole line.

Step 9 Construct the point where the perpendicular intersects the side, hide the line, and then construct the segment.

Step 10 To measure the ratio between the altitudes, select the shorter altitude, then the longer altitude, and choose Ratio in the Measure menu.

Investigate

1. Drag parts of your sketch and observe the ratio of the altitudes. Record your observations.

Sketch: Corresponding Medians in Similar Triangles

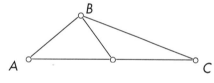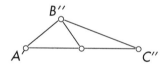

Step 10: Constructing the medians

Step 11 Delete or hide the altitudes, and construct a pair of corresponding medians. (To construct a median, construct a midpoint on a side. Then construct a segment from that midpoint to the opposite vertex.)

Step 12 Measure the ratio of the medians. (Remember to select the shorter one first.)

Investigate

2. Drag parts of your sketch and observe the ratio of the medians. Record your observations.

Sketch: Corresponding Angle Bisectors in Similar Triangles

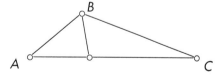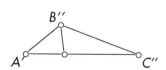

Step 13: Constructing the angle bisectors

Step 13 Delete or hide the medians, and construct a pair of corresponding angle bisectors. (To construct an angle bisector, select three points on the angle, with the vertex in the middle. Choose Angle Bisector in the Construct menu. This gives you a ray. Construct the point where the ray intersects the opposite side, hide the ray, and construct a segment.)

Step 14 Measure the ratio of the angle bisectors. (Remember to select the shorter one first.)

©1997 Key Curriculum Press

3. Drag parts of your sketch and observe the ratio of the angle bisectors. Record your observations.

4. Combine your observations about altitudes, medians, and angle bisectors into a single conjecture (C-105: Proportional Parts Conjecture).

Investigation 12.5.2: Another Look at the Angle Bisector

Sketch

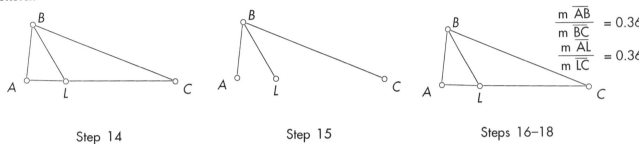

| Step 14 | Step 15 | Steps 16–18 |

Step 15 For this investigation, you only need one triangle with an angle bisector. Delete or hide the other parts of your sketch.

Step 16 Label the point where the angle bisector intersects the opposite side *L*. Make sure *L* is on side *AC*. (You may need to change your labels.) Hide side *AC*.

Step 17 Construct segments *AL* and *LC*.

Step 18 Measure the ratio of *AL* to *LC*.

Step 19 Measure the ratio of *AB* to *BC*.

Investigate

5. Drag parts of your sketch and compare the ratios. Write a conjecture to summarize your findings (C-106).

Lesson 12.6

Proportion with Area and Volume

If two figures are similar, one is simply a scaled version of another. How are the areas of similar figures related?

Investigation 12.6.1: Comparing Areas of Similar Figures

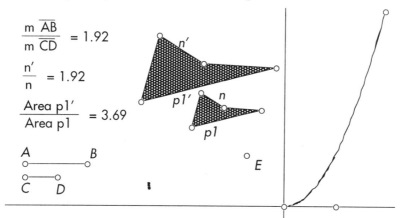

Sketch

Step 1   Construct segments $\overline{AB}$ and $\overline{CD}$, where $\overline{AB}$ is longer than $\overline{CD}$.

Step 2   Select $\overline{AB}$ and $\overline{CD}$ and mark AB/CD as a ratio using the Transform menu. While they're still selected, measure their ratio. This ratio will be the scale factor for your similar polygons.

Step 3   For your first polygon, construct any polygon and its interior.

Step 4   Construct a point outside the polygon and double-click the point with the selection arrow to mark it as a center.

Step 5   To make a second polygon that is similar to the first, select the sides, vertices, and interior of the first polygon and dilate the polygon by the marked ratio. If $\overline{AB}$ is longer than $\overline{CD}$, the image polygon will be bigger than the original polygon. Drag point B and experiment with changing the scale factor. Also experiment with dragging the center point.

Step 6   Select a side of the dilated polygon, then a corresponding side of the original polygon, and measure their ratio.

Step 7   Repeat step 6 using a different pair of corresponding sides. What is this ratio?

Step 8   Now you will compare the areas of the polygons in the same way. Take a minute to predict this ratio before you calculate it. Then measure the areas of both polygons. Use the calculator to find the ratio of the area of the dilated polygon to the area of the original. Did you get the ratio you predicted?

Step 9   Next, you will create a graph that plots the ratio of side lengths against the ratio of areas for different scale factors. To do this, select the measure of the ratio of the side lengths, then the calculation of the ratio of the areas. Choose Plot As (x, y) from the graph menu, then choose Trace Point from the Display menu.

Step 10   Drag point B to experiment with different scale factors. The point you plotted will trace out a graph of the side-length ratio against the area ratio for different pairs of similar figures.

Investigate

1. Drag *B* so that the ratio of the side lengths is 2/1 or 2. Use this information to complete the first column in a table like the one below. Then complete the rest of the table. The last column uses variables so that you can generalize for any scale factor *m/n*.

Ratios of Side Lengths and Ratios of Areas in Similar Figures

Ratio of corresponding side lengths	2	3	1	1/2	1/10	*m/n*
Ratio of areas						

2. Summarize the relationship between ratios of side lengths and ratios of areas in similar figures as the Proportional Area Conjecture (C-107).

3. Explain how the shape of the graph of the plotted points in your sketch supports Conjecture 107.

Explore More

1. Now you can compare similar shapes in 3 dimensions. How does the ratio of the volumes of similar solids compare to the ratio of the sides?

   a. One way to investigate this is by calculating the volumes of two cubes. Make one cube twice as long, twice as wide, and twice as tall as the other. Use your pencil to make sketches of a pair of such cubes and show your measurements. How do the volumes compare?

   b. Compare more similar solids if neccesary. Then summarize your conclusions as the Proportional Volume Conjecture (C-108).

Lesson 12.7

Proportional Segments by Parallel Lines

In this activity, you will cut two sides of a triangle with a segment. Then you will investigate measures of the new pieces in the construction.

Investigations 12.7.1 and 12.7.2

Sketch

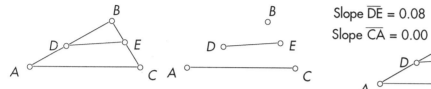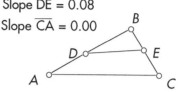

Steps 1 and 2	Step 3	Steps 4–7

Step 1   Construct any triangle *ABC*.

Step 2   Construct segment *DE* connecting sides *AB* and *BC*.

Step 3   Hide sides *AB* and *BC*.

Step 4   Construct segments *AD*, *DB*, *BE*, and *EC*.

Step 5   Select segments *DE* and *AC* and find their slope using the Measure menu.

Step 6   Select segment *AD*, then segment *DB*, and find their ratio using the Measure menu.

Step 7   Select segment *CE*, then segment *EB*, and find their ratio.

Investigate

1.   Drag point *E* until the slopes are equal. When the slopes are equal, $\overline{DE}$ is parallel to $\overline{AC}$. What can you say about $\triangle ABC$ and $\triangle DBE$? Explain.

2.   When $\overline{DE}$ is parallel to $\overline{AC}$ what do you observe about the ratios?

3.   Now investigate the converse of your observation in question 3: Drag a vertex to change the triangle, and drag point *E* until $\overline{DE}$ is no longer parallel to $\overline{AC}$. Now watch the ratios and drag point *E* until $\overline{DE}$ divides the sides proportionally. What can you say about segments *DE* and *AC*?

4.   Now combine your observations into a single conjecture (C-109: Parallel Proportionality Conjecture).

Investigation 12.7.3

Sketch

Step 1   In a new sketch, construct a triangle.

Step 2   Construct two points on the same side of the triangle.

Step 3   Select both points and another side of the triangle, and choose Parallel Line in the Construct menu.

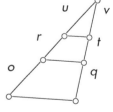

Step 4   Construct the two points where the parallel lines intersect the third side.

Step 5   Hide everything in your sketch except the points and the segment without any points on it.

Step 6   Connect nearby points with segments so your sketch looks like the picture above.

Step 7   Measure ratios of corresponding pairs of segments. For example, compare *u/r* and *v/t*. Also compare *u/o* and *v/q*. Measure three such pairs of ratios.

5. Drag vertices of your original triangle and observe the corresponding ratios. Record your observations as a conjecture (C-110: Extended Parallel Proportionality Conjecture).

Explore More

If three sides of one triangle are parallel to the three sides of another triangle, what do you think is true about the two triangles? Make a conjecture. Then make a construction to check your conjecture.

Trigonometry

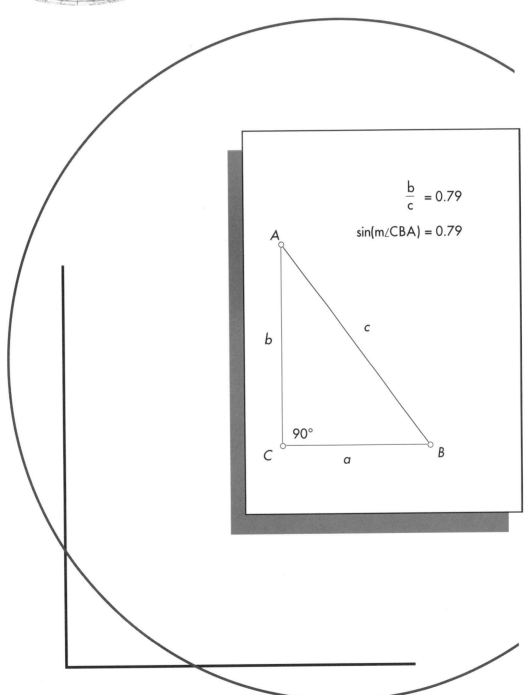

$$\frac{b}{c} = 0.79$$

$$\sin(m\angle CBA) = 0.79$$

Lesson 13.1

Trigonometric Ratios

In Chapter 10, you used the Pythagorean Theorem to find missing side lengths in right triangles—a powerful problem-solving tool. In Chapter 12, you used proportions in similar triangles to solve problems and to measure heights and distances indirectly. Right-triangle trigonometry builds on similar-triangle concepts to give you more ways to find unknown measures in triangles. In this lesson, you'll learn about trigonometric ratios and how you can use them.

Investigation 13.1

Sketch

First, you need to construct a right triangle using the method described in steps 1–5.

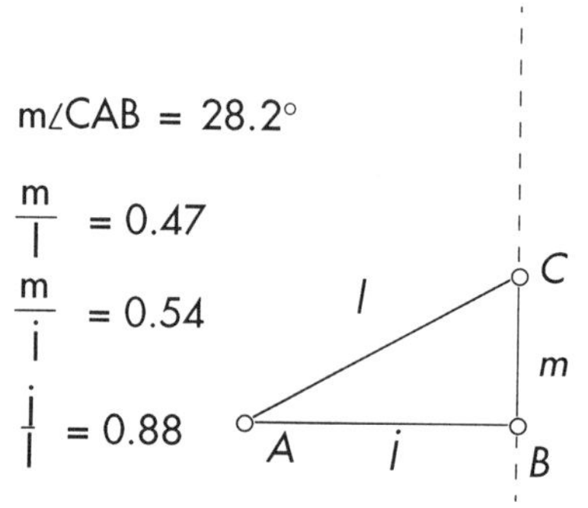

$m\angle CAB = 28.2°$

$\dfrac{m}{l} = 0.47$

$\dfrac{m}{j} = 0.54$

$\dfrac{j}{l} = 0.88$

Step 1   Construct $\overline{AB}$.

Step 2   Construct a line through point B perpendicular to $\overline{AB}$.

Step 3   Construct $\overline{AC}$, where point C is a point on the perpendicular line.

Step 4   Hide the line.

Step 5   Construct $\overline{BC}$ to finish the right triangle.

Step 6   Show the three segments' labels and, if necessary, change the labels to match the figure above. (To show a label, click on the segment once with the Text tool. Double-click on the label to change it.)

Step 7   Measure angle CAB.

Step 8   Measure the ratios m/j, m/l, and j/l. (To measure a ratio, select two segments in order, first the numerator and then the denominator.)

Investigate

Dragging point C should change the acute angles in your right triangle, and dragging point A or point B should change the size of the triangle without changing the angles.

1.   Drag point C. When the angles change, do the ratios also change?

2.   Drag point A or point B. What do you notice about the ratios when the angles don't change? Explain why you think this happens.

3.   Your observations in question 2 give you a very useful fact about right triangles. For any right triangle with a given acute angle, each ratio of side lengths has a given value, regardless of the size of the triangle. The three ratios you measured are called **tangent**, **sine**, and **cosine**. They are defined, for the triangle ABC above with acute angle A, as shown below left. Practice identifying sides by copying and completing the sine and cosine ratios below right.

$$\text{tangent } \angle A = \frac{\text{length of leg opposite } \angle A}{\text{length of leg adjacent to } \angle A}$$

$$\tan A = \frac{m}{j}$$

$$\text{sine } \angle A = \frac{\text{length of leg opposite } \angle A}{\text{length of hypotenuse}}$$

$$\sin A = \frac{-?-}{-?-}$$

$$\text{cosine } \angle A = \frac{\text{length of leg adjacent to } \angle A}{\text{length of hypotenuse}}$$

$$\cos A = \frac{-?-}{-?-}$$

4. Drag point *C* so that ∠*A* measures as close to 30° as you can get it. On your paper, write down approximate values for the tangent, sine, and cosine of 30°. Use the definitions above and refer to the calculations in your sketch to find these values.

5. Tangent, sine, and cosine functions can be found on all scientific calculators. You can use Sketchpad's calculator to check your answers to question 4. Make sure *m*∠*CAB* is still 30°. Double-click on a measure to get the calculator; then press the Functions pop-up menu. Choose tan[, click in the sketch on the measure of ∠*CAB*, and then click the close parenthesis in the calculator. Click OK. Use the same process to calculate the sine and cosine of ∠*CAB*. How do these three calculations compare to the ratios in your sketch?

6. Without measuring, figure out the measure of ∠*B* and write down that number. Use Sketchpad's calculator (or a pocket calculator) to find the sine of that angle measure. The sine of ∠*B* should be close to one of the trigonometric ratios for ∠*A*. Which one? Explain why this is so.

7. Before calculators became popular, people used tables of trigonometric ratios. By making such a table in Sketchpad, you can get a sense of some of the patterns in the trigonometric ratios. Follow the steps below.

Step 1 Drag point *C* so that *m*∠*BAC* = 0° (or close to it).

Step 2 Select these measurements or calculations in order: *m*∠*BAC*, tan(*m*∠*BAC*), sin(*m*∠*BAC*), and cos(*m*∠*BAC*).

Step 3 Choose Tabulate in the Measure menu.

Step 4 Drag point *C* to make *m*∠*BAC* = 10°.

Step 5 Double-click the table to add an entry.

Angle(CAB)	0.02	10.12	20.04	30.08	39.97	49.98	60.13	69.96	80.00
tan[Angle(CAB)]	0.00	0.18	0.36	0.58	0.84	1.19	1.74	2.74	5.67
sin[Angle(CAB)]	0.00	0.18	0.34	0.50	0.64	0.77	0.87	0.94	0.98
cos[Angle(CAB)]	1.00	0.98	0.94	0.87	0.77	0.64	0.50	0.34	0.17

Continue this process to make a table for angles in 10° increments from 0° to almost 90°. (You'll find that to make larger angles you'll have to make *AB* shorter.) Once you have your table, use it to answer the following questions.

a. Why couldn't you make *m*∠*BAC* exactly equal to 90°?

b. Even though you can't make *m*∠*BAC* exactly equal to 90°, what do you think is the value of tan 90°? Explain.

c. What's the greatest possible value for the sine of an angle? What angle has this value?

d. What's the least possible value for the sine of an angle? What angle has this value?

e. For what angle (not in your table) is the tangent equal to 1? Why?

f. For what angle are the sine and cosine equal? Why?

g. Suppose an angle has measure *x*. Complete this equation: sin *x* = cos (-?-).

Lesson 13.3

The Law of Sines

You saw in Lesson 13.1 how you can use trigonometric ratios to find unknown measures in a right triangle. In Chapter 5, you discovered that just a few parts (for example, ASA) determine a triangle. Is it possible to find unknown measures in *any* triangle if you know the right combination of measures? In this lesson, you'll discover a way to use the sine of an angle to find the area of a triangle. Then you'll derive a formula you can use to find all the measures in a triangle if you know the right combination of parts.

Investigation 13.3.1

Sketch

Step 1   Construct $\triangle ABC$. (It should not be a right triangle.)

Step 2   Use the Text tool to display the segment labels; then change each label so that the side opposite $\angle A$ is labeled a, the side opposite $\angle B$ is labeled b, and the side opposite $\angle C$ is labeled c. (To change a label, double-click on it with the Text tool.)

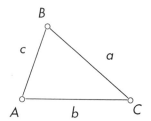

a = 2.977 cm
b = 2.928 cm
c = 2.053 cm
m∠BAC = 70.94°
sin(m∠BAC) = 0.945

Step 3   Measure the lengths of the three sides, and measure $\angle ACB$. (To measure an angle, select three points, with the vertex your middle selection.)

Step 4   Use the calculator to calculate sin($m\angle ACB$). (You can find the sine function in the Functions pop-up menu in the calculator.)

Investigate

1.   Recall the formula you used in Chapter 9 for the area of a triangle. Write down that formula.

2.   In your sketch, you haven't constructed or measured the height of the triangle, but you can calculate the area of the triangle without knowing the height if you use trigonometry. Start by figuring out an expression that gives the height of the triangle in terms of sin A and one or more of the side lengths you measured. (Draw the height in your triangle, if that helps you see how it's related to the angle and the side lengths.) Write down that expression: $h = $ -?-.

3.   Now use the calculator to create an expression that gives the area of the triangle. When you think you have the correct calculation, test it by constructing the polygon interior and measuring the area. If your calculation doesn't match your measurement, analyze what you might have done wrong and try again. When you have it right, write a conjecture stating your formula for the area of a triangle in terms of side lengths and an angle (C-111).

Investigation 13.3.2

Investigate

4.   Use what you discovered in Investigation 13.3.1 to explain why these equations are true:

$$(1/2)(bc)\sin A = (1/2)(ac)\sin B = (1/2)(ab)\sin C$$

5.   Multiply each expression in question 4 by 2 (to cancel the 1/2) and divide each expression by abc. The simplified equation statement you're left with is the law of sines (C-112). Write down the law of sines.

Geometric Proof

Sequences of Proofs

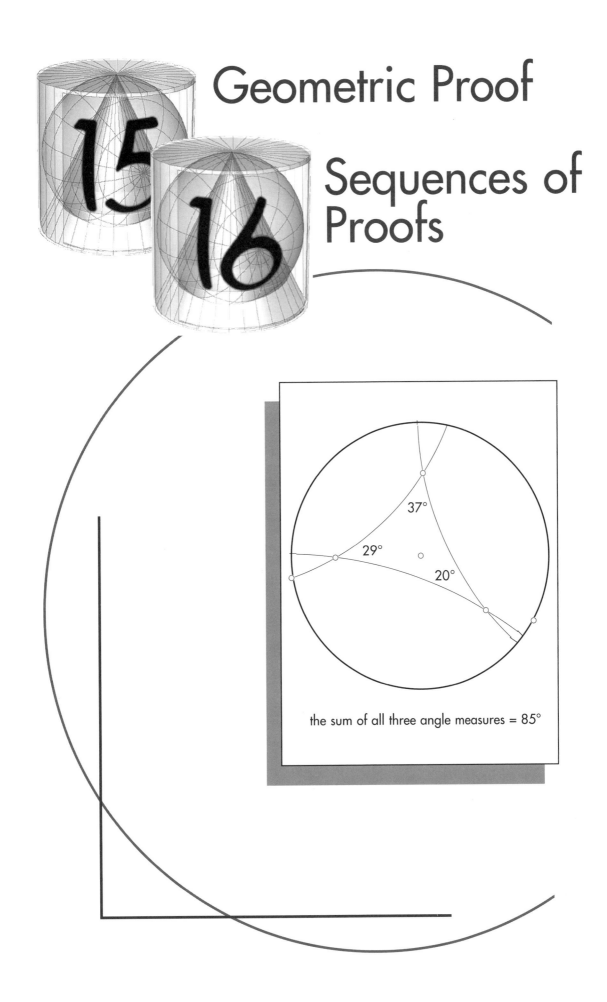

the sum of all three angle measures = 85°

Project

Non-Euclidean Geometries

When Euclid built his deductive system of geometry theorems in his book *The Elements,* he started with a set of mostly simple assumptions, called postulates. He considered the postulates to be self-evident, and he used them to prove theorems. Then he used proven theorems to prove more theorems until he had a massive volume of geometric facts. The conjectures you've made are based on Euclid's geometry. However, over time, mathematicians have been dissatisfied with one of Euclid's postulates. Somehow, Euclid's fifth postulate seems less than self-evident. It states:

> If two straight lines lying in a plane are met by another line and if the sum of the interior angles on one side is less than two right angles, then the straight lines, if extended sufficiently, will meet on the side on which the sum of the angles is less than two right angles.

A simpler, logically equivalent statement called Playfair's axiom makes the postulate a little easier to believe. Playfair's axiom states: "Through a point not on a given line there passes at most one line that is parallel to the given line." Before you read further, make a quick sketch on a piece of paper to see if you agree with this axiom.

Still, however the postulate was stated, mathematicians long sought to prove it using Euclid's other four postulates or to replace it with something more self-evident. Finally, in the early nineteenth century, over 2000 years after Euclid lived, mathematicians discovered that if you assume the postulate is not true, you can build new and different deductive systems of geometry in which some theorems from Euclidean geometry remain the same and some are quite different. These non-Euclidean geometries typically replace Euclid's fifth postulate with one or the other of the following assumptions:

Assumption 1: Through a given point not on a given line there pass more than one line parallel to the given line.

Assumption 2: Through a given point not on a given line there pass no lines parallel to the given line.

You might have experimented with spherical geometry, in which the second assumption is true. In this activity, you'll play with a geometry based on one of these assumptions (it will be up to you to figure out which assumption). Instead of taking place in an infinite plane, this geometry takes place within a disk, called the Poincaré disk, devised by French mathematician Henri Poincaré (1854–1912).

Investigation: The Poincaré Disk

Sketch

Step 1   Open the sketch Poincaré Disk Starter (Mac) or ch15\poincare.gsp (Windows).

Step 2   Set the Poincaré folder as your Script tool folder. To do this, choose Preferences in the Display menu and click More. In the Advanced Preferences dialog, under Set Script Tool Folder, click Set. (You may first have to click Clear.) Navigate in the pop-up menu to find the Poincaré folder. Click the Set button. Click Continue; then click OK to dismiss the Preferences dialog.

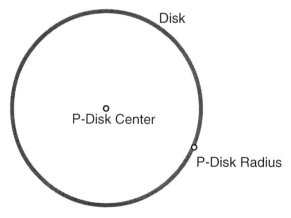

Step 3   You should now have a tool at the bottom of your toolbox that looks like a double arrowhead. Press on this tool. You should see a menu with the following tools listed: Circle By Center+Point, Line, Measure Angle, Measure Distance, Segment, and Other.

Investigate

You're now ready to start playing with Poincaré geometry. As you do, keep these things in mind:

- As long as you're doing Poincaré geometry, the only tools you should use are those in the Script tool folder and Sketchpad's Point tool. Don't use any other tools, and don't use the Construct, Transform, Measure, or Graph menus. In the investigation, whenever you're asked to construct a line, segment, or circle, use the Poincaré tools in the Script tool to construct these objects.

- Everything you construct should be inside the disk. If you construct or drag anything outside the disk, don't expect the rules of Poincaré geometry to apply.

- A true Poincaré line should be able to pass through the center of the disk, but you may find that when you drag lines so they pass through the center, they disappear momentarily. This is not a property of Poincaré disk geometry; it is just a limitation of the line script.

- The Measure Angle tool and the Measure Distance tool don't display labels of the objects they measure. If you need to keep track of which measurements measure what, use the Text tool to change the labels of the measurements.

- If comments at the bottom of the sketch get in your way while you're using a Script tool, turn off Show Comments in the Script tool pop-up menu.

1. Take a few minutes to just play with the tools to get a feel for how to use them and what they do. Draw segments, lines, and circles with the Script tools and drag the figures around. Try measuring distances and angles using the Script tools. Write down four or five observations you make about this geometry.

2. Now it's time to explore Poincaré geometry more systematically. Close the sketch without saving; then open Poincaré Disk Starter (Mac) or ch15\poincare.gsp (Windows) again so that you have a blank disk. Draw a line. (Don't forget to use the Line Script tool, not Sketchpad's Line tool.) Describe the line and how it meets the edge of the disk.

3. Construct a point not on the line. (The Point tool is the only Sketchpad tool that's fair game.) How many lines can you draw through the point that don't intersect the line? Which of the two assumptions listed in the introduction is Poincaré disk geometry based on?

4. In the Poincaré disk, distances get distorted. One way to see this is to look at how circles behave. Construct a circle centered somewhere other than at the center of the disk. Drag its center and observe the circle's behavior. On a Poincaré circle, as on a Euclidean circle, all points are equally distant from the center. All radii are equal. But it doesn't look that way, does it? Which radii look shorter to your Euclidean eye: radii that go toward the center of the disk, or radii that go toward the edge of the disk?

5. Now it's time for a non-Euclidean conjecture. Close the sketch without saving; then open Poincaré Disk Starter (Mac) or ch15\poincare.gsp (Windows) again so that you have a blank disk. Draw a triangle. Measure the three angles and use the calculator to sum them. Drag the vertices of the triangle. You should observe that the angle sum, unlike that in a Euclidean triangle, is not a constant. What range can this sum have? Write a conjecture.

6. Investigate the Isosceles Triangle Conjecture in the Poincaré disk. To construct an isosceles triangle, construct a circle and two radii; then connect the radius endpoints for the third side of your triangle. Remember that distances get distorted, so your triangle may not look isosceles. Measure distances to confirm that it is. Then measure angles and make a conjecture about base angles in an isosceles triangle.

7. Devise and perform another investigation of your own on the Poincaré disk. Try some of the tools in the Other submenu of the Script tool menu. Describe what you did and what you discovered.

Lesson 16.7

Midsegment Conjectures

In this lesson, you'll investigate quadrilaterals formed by connecting the midpoints of other quadrilaterals. Then you'll use the Triangle Midsegment Theorem to prove the conjectures you make. Start with the first investigation; then choose one or more of the quadrilaterals in question 4 to investigate.

Investigation: An Arbitrary Quadrilateral

Sketch

Step 1   Use the Segment tool to construct quadrilateral *ABCD*.

Step 2   Construct the midpoints of the four sides.

Step 3   Connect the midpoints to construct another quadrilateral, *EFGH*. Make the sides of this midpoint quadrilateral a different color or thickness than quadrilateral *ABCD*.

Step 4   Measure the four side lengths of this midpoint quadrilateral.

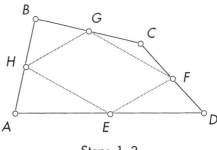

Steps 1–3

Investigate

1. Drag vertices of your original quadrilateral. What kind of quadrilateral does the midpoint quadrilateral appear to be? How do the measurements support that conjecture?

2. Sketchpad leaves little doubt that the conjecture you made in question 1 is true. A proof can help explain *why* the conjecture is true. One way to prove the conjecture is to use the Triangle Midsegment Theorem. Start by drawing diagonal *BD*.

    a. $\overline{GF}$ is the midsegment of $\triangle BCD$. How are $\overline{BD}$ and $\overline{GF}$ related?

    b. $\overline{HE}$ is a midsegment of $\triangle ABD$. How are $\overline{BD}$ and $\overline{HE}$ related?

    c. How are $\overline{GF}$ and $\overline{HE}$ related?

    d. Draw diagonal *AC*. Describe how $\overline{HG}$ and $\overline{EF}$ are related and explain why.

3. Use your answers to question 2 to write a paragraph, flow-chart, or two-column proof of the midpoint quadrilateral conjecture.

Investigation: Special Quadrilaterals

Investigate

4. Choose one or more of the following quadrilaterals to investigate: rectangle, rhombus, isosceles trapezoid, square, or kite. Make sure at least one group picks each quadrilateral so you can summarize your findings as a class. Investigate the midpoint quadrilateral of your chosen quadrilateral in the following way:

    a. Construct your chosen quadrilateral.

    b. Construct its midpoint quadrilateral.

    c. Drag vertices of the original quadrilateral and make a conjecture about the midpoint quadrilateral. Make measurements to confirm your conjecture, if necessary.

    d. Prove your conjecture.

Explore More

The proofs you did can help you discover more about midpoint quadrilaterals. In the investigations above, you discovered that some special quadrilaterals have special parallelograms for midpoint quadrilaterals. But are those the only quadrilaterals whose midpoint quadrilaterals are special parallelograms? Try one or more of the following investigations. Hint: Just as diagonals were the key to the proofs you did in the investigations above, diagonals are the key to these Explore More investigations.

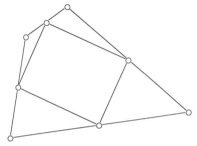

1. Name two special quadrilaterals that have rectangles for midpoint quadrilaterals. What do these special quadrilaterals have in common? Describe the most general quadrilateral whose midpoint quadrilateral is a rectangle. Construct it with Sketchpad.

2. Name two special quadrilaterals that have rhombuses for midpoint quadrilaterals. What do these special quadrilaterals have in common? Describe the most general quadrilateral whose midpoint quadrilateral is a rhombus. Construct it with Sketchpad.

3. What special quadrilateral has a square for its midpoint quadrilateral? What properties do the diagonals of this special quadrilateral have? Describe the most general quadrilateral whose midpoint quadrilateral is a square. Construct it with Sketchpad.

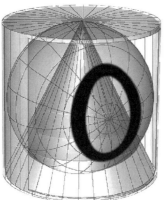

Geometric Art

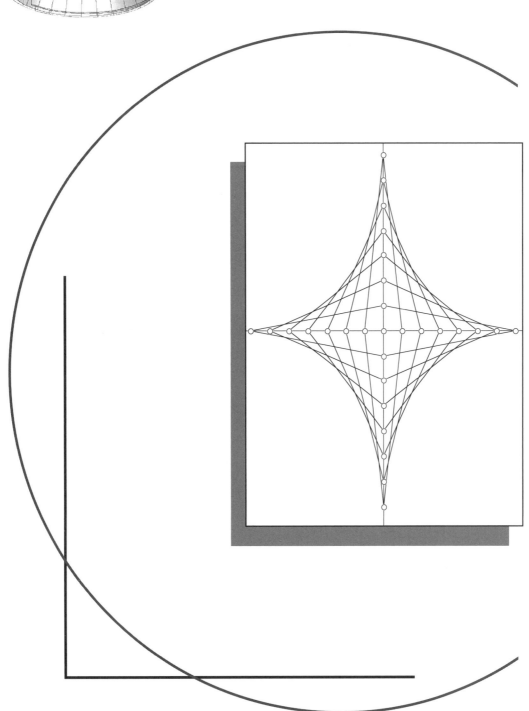

Lesson 0.2

Line Designs

You can use straight lines to create designs that appear to curve. Example A on page 7 of *Discovering Geometry* is an example of the art of curve stitching, developed by nineteenth-century mathematician and teacher Mary Everest Boole. You can make curve-stitched designs using string and cardboard. In this activity, you'll learn how to use Sketchpad to create a dynamic version of a curve-stitched design.

Sketch

In steps 1–10, you'll construct two segments with a common endpoint and with equally spaced points along them.

Step 1   Construct point *A* and another point, point *B*, just to the right of it.

Step 2   Select, in order, point *A* and point *B* and choose Mark Vector in the Transform menu.

Step 3   Select point *B* and choose Translate in the Transform menu. Translate by the marked vector to construct point *B′*.

Step 4   Translate point *B′* by the same marked vector to construct point *B″*. Keep translating the most recently constructed point until you have about ten points along a line.

Step 5   Drag point *A* or point *B* to see how they affect the other points.

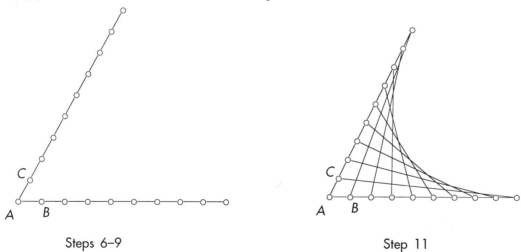

Steps 1–5

Step 6   Construct point *C* just above point *A*.

Step 7   Select, in order, point *A* and point *C* and choose Mark Vector in the Transform menu.

Step 8   Translate point *C* by this marked vector and repeat to construct the same number of points as you constructed in the direction of vector *AB* (about ten).

Step 9   Draw a segment from point *A* to the last point at the end of each row of points as shown in the figure below left.

Step 10   Drag point *C* to see how it affects the other points.

Steps 6–9   Step 11

Step 11   Draw segments to connect points as shown in the figure above right.

Step 12   Hide the points that you don't need (but don't hide points *A*, *B*, or *C*) and add color to the lines in your design.

Step 13 Double-click on the segment that passes from point *A* through point *C* to mark it as a reflection mirror.

Step 14 Select all the segments and choose Reflect in the Transform menu.

Step 15 Double-click on the segment that passes from point *A* through point *B* to mark it as a mirror; then reflect all the segments again to make a design like the one shown below.

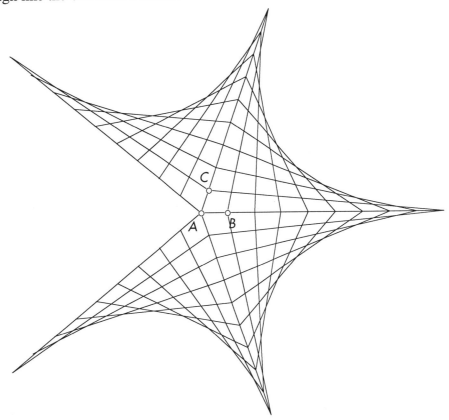

Investigate

1. The design at right has just one line of symmetry. Where is it?

2. Drag points *A*, *B*, and *C* to see how they change your design.

   a. Manipulate your design so that it has two lines of symmetry. Describe the lines.

   b. Manipulate your design so that it has four lines of symmetry. Describe the lines.

   c. Manipulate your design so that it has three lines of symmetry. Describe the lines.

Explore More

Open a new sketch and experiment with this method or other methods to make different line designs.

Lesson 0.3

Daisy Designs

A daisy design is a simple design that you can create using only a compass. From the basic daisy, you can create more complex designs based on the regular hexagon.

Sketch

Step 1   Construct circle *AB* (a circle with center *A* and radius control point *B*).

Step 2   Construct circle *BA*. Be sure you start your circle with the cursor positioned at point *B* and that you don't let go of the mouse until the cursor is positioned at point *A*.

Step 3   Construct the two points of intersection of these circles.

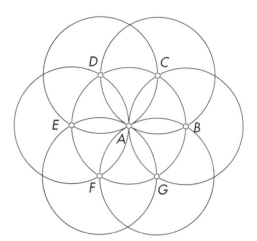

Step 4   Using the intersection points as centers, continue constructing circles to existing points. All these circles should have equal radii. When you're done, your sketch should look like the figure above right.

Step 5   If your last circle refuses to be constructed, you're probably releasing the mouse on the intersection of three circles. In this case, select two circles and construct their intersection with the Construct menu. Then use this point to construct your final circle.

Step 6   Use the Segment tool to add some lines to your design; then drag point *B* and observe how your design changes.

At this point, you could construct polygon interiors and experiment with shading and color. You could also construct arcs (select a circle and two points on it) and arc sector and arc segment interiors (select an arc). However, you can probably get better results by printing out the basic design and adding color and shading by hand.

The six points of your daisy define six vertices of a regular hexagon. You can use these points as the basis for hexagon or star designs like these shown below. Once you have all the lines and polygon interiors you want, you can hide unneeded points. Don't hide your original two points, though, as you can use these points to manipulate your figure.

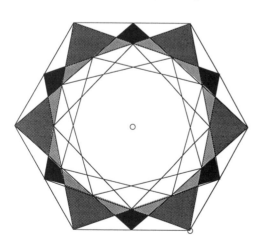

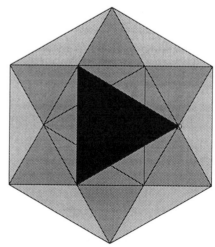

Lesson 0.4

Op Art

A tumbling block design is commonly found in Amish quilt patterns. It's an example of op art because of the interesting optical effect suggested by its name. You can create a tumbling block design very efficiently with Sketchpad using translations.

Sketch

Step 1   Construct a regular hexagon. Use your own method or a script such as 6/Hexagon (Inscribed) (Mac) or ch00\6inscrib.gss (Windows).

Step 2   If you used a script that constructs the hexagon's interior, click on the interior to select it; then delete it.

Step 3   Construct the center of the hexagon (if it doesn't already exist).

Step 4   Construct segments and two polygon interiors to make your hexagon look like the figure at right. To construct a polygon interior, select the vertices of the region whose interior you wish to construct; then choose Polygon Interior in the Construct menu.

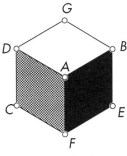

Steps 1–4

In steps 5–7, you'll translate this figure to create a row of these blocks.

Step 5   Select points *D* and *B*, in that order, and choose Mark Vector in the Transform menu.

Step 6   Select All; then hold down Shift and click on each of the points to deselect them. Translate by vector *DB*.

Step 7   Translate the new block two more times so that you have a row of four blocks. Drag a control point of your original hexagon if you need to scale your blocks.

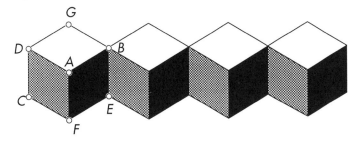

Steps 5–7

Step 8   Mark *DF* as vector.

Step 9   Select All (including the points) and translate the row of blocks by vector *DF*.

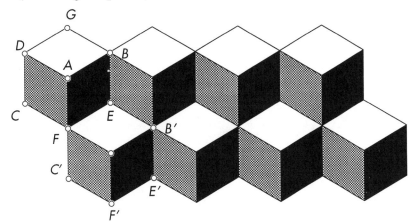

Step 10 Mark *GC′* as vector.

Step 11 Select All and translate the two rows of blocks by vector *GC′* to create four rows total.

Step 12 To make your design neater, hide all the points except those that control your original block.

Step 13 Drag point *B* and observe how you can change your design.

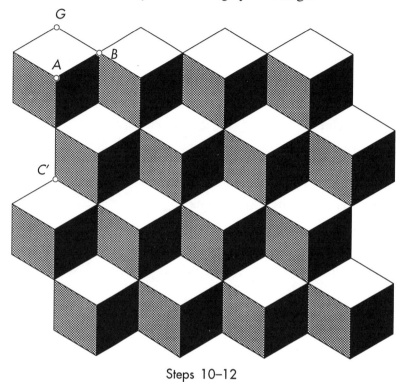

Steps 10–12

Investigate

1. Describe the shapes that make up your design.

2. Describe the optical effect of this design.

Explore More

1. Make an action button to animate point *B* around a circle. To do this, draw a small circle somewhere near point *B*. Select the circle and point *B* and choose Animation from the Action Button submenu in the Edit menu. Double-click the Animation button to make it work.

2. Use Sketchpad to make another op art design of your own.

Lesson 0.7

Islamic Art

In this activity, you'll construct a square-based knot design similar to designs created by Islamic artists.

Sketch

Step 1   Construct a square and its center using a script such as 4/Square (Inscribed) (Mac) or ch00\4inscrib.gss (Windows). If your script constructs the square's interior, click on the interior and delete it.

Step 2   Construct the midpoints of the sides of this square and connect them to construct a smaller square within the square.

Step 3   Double-click the center to mark it as a center for rotation.

Step 4   Select the entire figure and choose Rotate in the Transform menu. Rotate by 45°.

Step 5   Construct eight points of intersection where the small squares intersect and eight more points where the large squares intersect.

Step 6   Select the entire figure and in the Display menu choose Line Weight: Dashed.

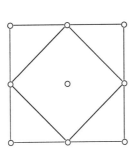

Steps 1 and 2

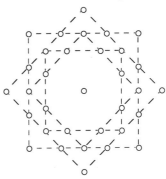

Steps 3–6

Now you have the basic outline of the design, and you're ready to draw over it to make it appear knotted.

Step 7   Make sure nothing is selected in the sketch; then in the Display menu choose Line Weight: Thick. Nothing should change in your sketch, but the next segment you draw will be thick.

Step 8   Study your design and plan out how you're going to draw solid lines over some of the dashed ones so that the design appears as two knotted squares. Try it on your own, or follow the next step to see one way to do it.

Step 9   Starting from the topmost corner and going counterclockwise, draw segments to show the top corner going over the other square, then under, over, under, over, and so on.

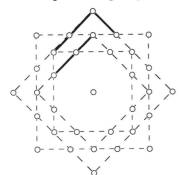
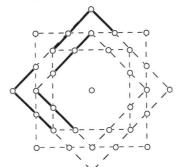
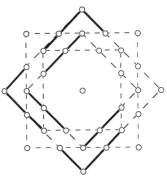

Discovering Geometry with The Geometer's Sketchpad **123**

Step 10 When you've finished drawing segments going over and under on both squares, your design should look like the one shown below left.

Step 11 Put finishing touches on the design: Click on each of the dashed segments where they remain visible (holding down Shift) and choose Hide Segments in the Display menu. Construct polygon interiors to add color or shading to the design. (See below right.)

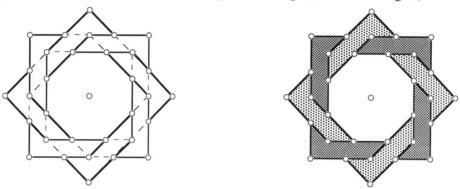

Now that you have the basic design, you're ready to make a repeating pattern like the patterns so often found in Islamic art.

Step 12 Select, in order, the points shown with labels *A* and *B* in the figure at right. In the Transform menu, choose Mark Vector.

Step 13 Select the entire figure; then, in the Transform menu, choose Translate to translate your design by the marked vector. Repeat the translation so that you have a row of three designs.

Step 14 Mark vector *CD*, select all, and translate the row of three designs twice so that you have three rows.

Step 15 Construct other polygon interiors to fill in other areas with color as you wish. Drag the center point of the top left design to manipulate the design until it's aligned and sized the way you like it. Hide any points you don't need.

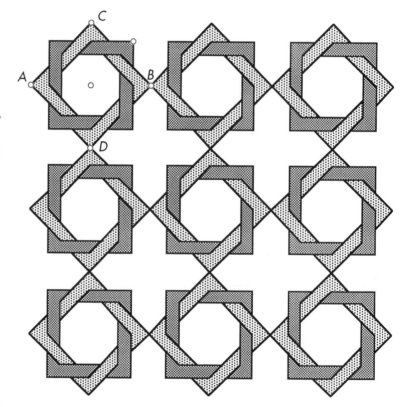

Explore More

Experiment with making another Islamic-style design of your own using Sketchpad.

Lesson 0.8

Perspective

Even though a piece of paper or a computer screen is flat, you can draw figures that appear three-dimensional on these two-dimensional surfaces by using perspective drawing. In three dimensions, objects that are farther away appear smaller to us. Perspective drawing takes advantage of this principle to make flat drawings appear to have depth.

Follow these steps to draw a box with two-point perspective. Labels are shown to clarify these directions, but you probably won't want labels on your drawing.

Sketch

Step 1   Draw a long horizontal line segment *AB*. This will be your **horizon line**, and its endpoints will be the **vanishing points** of your perspective box.

Step 2   Draw a short, vertical segment *CD* below your horizon line. This will be the front edge of your box. Change its line weight to dashed using the Display menu.

Step 3   Construct $\overline{CA}$, $\overline{DA}$, $\overline{CB}$, and $\overline{DB}$.

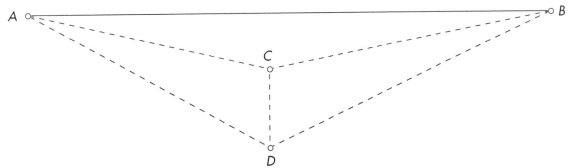

Step 4   Construct point *E* on $\overline{DA}$ and point *F* on $\overline{DB}$.

Step 5   Select points *E* and *F* and segment *CD* and choose Parallel Line in the Construct menu to construct two lines parallel to $\overline{CD}$.

Step 6   Construct $\overline{GB}$ and $\overline{HA}$ where points *G* and *H* are the new points of intersection with $\overline{CA}$ and $\overline{CB}$.

Step 7   Construct point *I* at the point of intersection of $\overline{GB}$ and $\overline{HA}$.

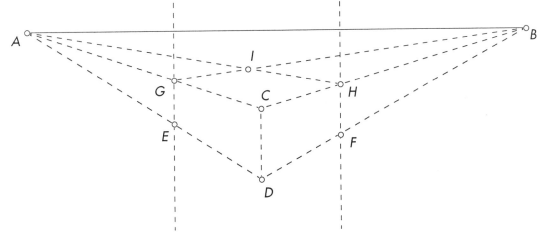

Step 8 Change the line weight of $\overline{CD}$ to thick; then construct $\overline{GI}$, $\overline{IH}$, $\overline{HF}$, $\overline{FD}$, $\overline{DE}$, $\overline{EG}$, $\overline{GC}$, and $\overline{CH}$.

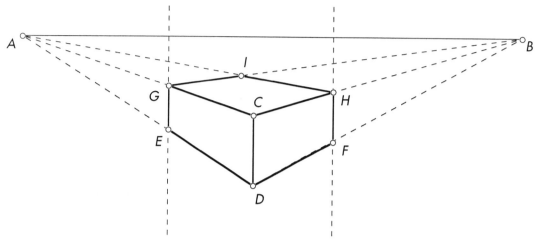

Step 9 Hide all the dashed lines and segments to leave just your box and the horizon line.

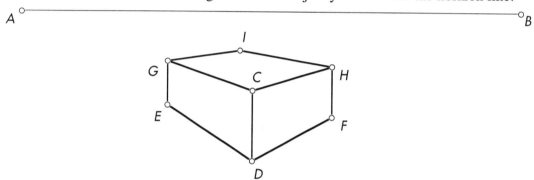

Step 10 Try moving various parts of your box, your horizon segment, and the vanishing points. If you move the front edge of your box above the horizon segment, you'll discover that you haven't created the bottom of your box. Continue sketching to construct the missing edges as shown. (Hint: Start by constructing a dashed segment from point E to point B.)

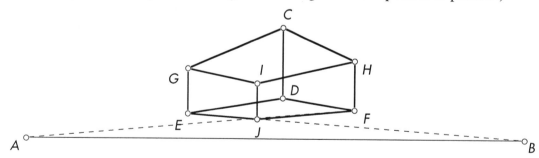

Step 11 Hide unwanted points and segments. (Points A, B, C, D, E, and F will be the only draggable points.)

Lesson
Guides

Introduction to The Geometer's Sketchpad

Example Sketches

None

Discovering Geometry Correlation/Lesson Guide

This lesson does not correlate directly with any lesson in *Discovering Geometry*. It is intended to be students' first experience with Sketchpad, so plan to use it the first day you have access to the computer lab, the first day you want a break from using the book, or whatever works best. Using this lesson in conjunction with Lesson 2.1: Building Blocks of Geometry makes some sense, since students will be working with many of these "building blocks" on Sketchpad.

The lesson consists of two parts, the first Investigate section is very open ended, while the second section, The Geometer's Sketchpad Checklist, is slightly less so. Use the sections in two consecutive class periods, or give students the checklist part way through one class period.

Keep in mind that the *User Guide and Reference Manual* that accompanied Sketchpad contains an entire section of guided tours that you can also use as beginning lessons. These are more structured than the activity here. If it is your first experience teaching with Sketchpad, pick the option you feel most comfortable with and that best matches your teaching style.

Investigate

You will decide how long to let students investigate freely. Some teachers have found this valuable for as long as two entire class periods, while others have found it worthwhile only for 15 minutes. This depends very much on the size of your class, your student's comfort level with few directions, and your own comfort level with this. Students learn from this experience that they can figure out a great deal about using Sketchpad without your help. Teachers find that starting with a lesson of this kind makes classtime in the computer lab more productive for the rest of the year, since students develop the confidence to figure out answers to many of their own questions and do not wait with their hand up for teacher help every time they get stuck.

Like most classrooms, yours will probably have every type of student from the computer enthusiast to the computer phobic. For this reason, it is best not to allow any student to have their own computer for this activity so that nobody works alone, and it is essential that students share the mouse. You might want to enforce this by calling out "switch mouse" every 10 minutes, or by flashing the lights, or by some other attention-getting means. Two students per computer is ideal, if you have enough machines.

Some teachers provide a bit more structure in this opening activity. For example, one teacher counts each entry on the student's list of completed tasks as a point, another requires that each pair meet with a neighboring pair after a certain amount of time to share discoveries.

The Geometer's Sketchpad Checklist

Emphasize to students that there are some difficult constructions sprinkled throughout this list that they could not possibly figure out on the first day. There may well be constructions that you cannot do yourself yet (for example, building the rolling car is quite a challenge!) Don't be afraid to tell students there are parts of the program you do not yet understand. Emphasize that the list does not go in order from easy to hard, and that students should read through the whole list to look for tasks they can do.

If you have time, have students rotate through different groups and share tasks from their list. By comparing lists, students can easily find tasks that are checked on only one student's sheet, and that person can show the others how to do the task.

You may want to require students to keep this list in their notebooks and update it throughout the year. You can also use this list for performance assessment at any time during the year. Tell students that you will pick any item on the list that they should have checked (you might be specific about which ones these are), and ask them to demonstrate that task at a computer. If you do only a couple of these performance assessments every lab day, it won't take too much classtime and you can eventually get to every student individually.

Lesson 2.6

Defining Triangles

Required Sketches

- Classify Triangles (Mac) or ch02\classtri.gsp (Windows)
- Altitude/Median (Mac) or ch02\altmed.gsp (Windows)

Discovering Geometry Correlation/Lesson Guide

You could use this lesson in place of Lesson 2.6 in *Discovering Geometry,* but this lesson would probably work better as a review or extension of the book lesson. DG Investigation 2.6 is broken into two parts here. Sketch A covers acute, obtuse, right, scalene, isosceles, and equilateral triangles. Sketch B covers definitions of median and altitude in a triangle.

This activity doesn't require much Sketchpad savvy. Students will be working mostly with premade sketches. All students need to be able to do is measure angles and lengths. This lesson and Lesson 2.7, however, do help introduce students to Sketchpad constructions. Novice users, when asked to construct right triangles, for example, most often draw arbitrary triangles and manipulate them until they approximate right triangles. The experience students get with these sketches should give students a sense of how figures can be constructed with proper constraints according to their definitions. Explore More asks students to try some of these constructions themselves.

Be sure to summarize the lesson by agreeing on the definitions in questions 17, 18, and 20 as a class and having students add these definitions to their definition lists.

Investigate

1. Answers will vary, but most students should find $\triangle ABC$ to be the least constrained.

2. Answers will vary. The equilateral triangle, $\triangle GHI$, should get many votes for most constrained.

3. A triangle can have three acute angles. It will always have at least two.

4. A triangle can have no more than one obtuse angle.

5. $\triangle DEF$ (the isosceles triangle) can be acute or obtuse.

6. $\triangle LMN$ is always a right triangle.

7. $\triangle GHI$ is always equiangular.

8. $\triangle ABC$ is usually a scalene triangle.

9. $\triangle LMN$ (the right triangle) is usually scalene.

10. $\triangle DEF$ is always isosceles. $\triangle GHI$ (the equilateral triangle) is also isosceles.

11. $\triangle GHI$ is always equilateral.

12. Possible

13. Not possible

14. Not possible

15. Possible

16. Possible

17. An acute triangle is a triangle with three acute angles.

    An obtuse triangle is a triangle with an obtuse angle.

    A right triangle is a triangle with a right angle.

    A scalene triangle is a triangle with three sides of different lengths.

    An isosceles triangle is a triangle with at least two sides the same length.

    An equilateral triangle is a triangle with three sides the same length.

18. A median of a triangle is a segment connecting the midpoint of a side to the opposite vertex.

19. Segment BE falls outside the triangle whenever $\angle A$ or $\angle C$ is obtuse.

20. An altitude of a triangle is a perpendicular segment from a vertex to the opposite side or the line containing the opposite side.

21. Every triangle has three altitudes and three medians: one of each from each vertex.

Lesson 2.7

Special Quadrilaterals

Required Sketches

- Trapezoid & Kite (Mac) or ch02\trapkite.gsp (Windows)
- Special Quads (Mac) or ch02\spquads.gsp (Windows)

Discovering Geometry Correlation/Lesson Guide

Use this lesson in place of, or as an extension to, Lesson 2.7 in *Discovering Geometry*. DG Investigation 2.7 is broken into two parts here. Sketch A covers definitions of trapezoid and kite, and Sketch B covers definitions of parallelogram, rhombus, rectangle, and square.

Note that in *Discovering Geometry* students define *trapezoid* and *kite* exclusively. That is, a trapezoid cannot be a parallelogram and a kite cannot be a rhombus. Exclusive definitions of *trapezoid* and *kite* are standard in most books, yet a Sketchpad trapezoid can be manipulated into a parallelogram, and a Sketchpad kite can be manipulated into a rhombus. Questions 2 and 4 explain those restrictions to the definitions of *trapezoid* and *kite*. On the other hand, parallelogram definitions are inclusive. That is, a square is a rhombus and a rectangle, and rhombuses and rectangles are both parallelograms. These inclusive definitions are more consistent with Sketchpad constructions. For example, a construction with just the constraints of a parallelogram can be manipulated into a rhombus, rectangle, or square.

Be sure to summarize the lesson by agreeing on definitions as a class. Contrast the exclusive definitions of *trapezoid* and *kite* with the inclusive definitions of the different types of parallelograms.

Construction Tips: Investigation 2.7, Sketch A

Students use a premade sketch for this investigation.

Step 3: To measure a slope, select a straight object (segment, ray, or line) and choose slope in the Measure menu.

Investigate

1. In general, exactly one pair of sides in the trapezoid are parallel.
2. A trapezoid is a quadrilateral with exactly one pair of parallel sides.
3. In general, two pairs of consecutive sides are equal in length.
4. A kite is a quadrilateral with exactly two pairs of distinct congruent consecutive sides.
5. A parallelogram is a quadrilateral in which both pairs of opposite sides are parallel.
6. A rectangle is a quadrilateral with four congruent angles.
7. A rhombus is a quadrilateral with four congruent sides.
8. A square is a quadrilateral with four congruent sides and four congruent angles.
9. A rhombus that is also a rectangle is a square.
10. A rectangle that is also a rhombus is a square.
11. A square is an equiangular rhombus or an equilateral rectangle.
12. A parallelogram is sometimes a square.
13. A rectangle is sometimes a rhombus.
14. A square is always a rhombus.
15. A rectangle is always a parallelogram.
16. A parallelogram that is not a rectangle is never a square.

Lesson 3.2
Constructing Perpendicular Bisectors

Example Sketches

• Perpendicular Bisector (Mac) or ch03\perpbis.gsp (Windows)

Discovering Geometry Correlation/Lesson Guide

This lesson covers all the conjectures in Lesson 3.2 in *Discovering Geometry*. However, in the exercise set, students are asked to do patty paper and compass/straightedge constructions. Refer students to the investigations in the text for guidance on how to do these constructions.

Construction Tips: Investigation 3.2.1

Step 3: Make sure students use points *B* and *A* for circle *BA* instead of merely constructing a circle with center *B* that happens to pass through *A* but is defined by a third point.

Investigate

1. Students should confirm visually that point *E* is the midpoint of segment *AB*.

2. If a point is on the perpendicular bisector of a segment, then it is equally distant from the endpoints (C-1: Perpendicular Bisector Conjecture).

3. A point not on a segment's perpendicular bisector is not equally distant from the segment's endpoints.

4. If a point is equally distant from the endpoints of a segment, then it is on the perpendicular bisector of the segment (C-2: Converse of the Perpendicular Bisector Conjecture).

Explore More

1. Draw a segment. Construct its midpoint. Select the midpoint and the segment and choose Perpendicular Line in the Construct menu.

2. Line *AB* is the perpendicular bisector of segment *CC'*.

Constructing Perpendiculars

Example Sketches

- Shortest Distance (Mac) or ch03\shortdis.gsp (Windows)

- Sewer River Problem (Mac) or ch03\swrprob.gsp (Windows)

Discovering Geometry Correlation/Lesson Guide

Lesson 3.3 in *Discovering Geometry* covers two investigations besides this one. In DG Investigation 3.3.1, students discover how to construct a perpendicular through a point not on a given line using compass and straightedge. In DG Investigation 3.3.3, students discover how to construct perpendiculars using patty papers. Neither of those investigations concludes in a conjecture, so you could replace Lesson 3.3 in the book with this Investigation 3.3.2. If you do, assign Investigations 3.3.1 and 3.3.3 with the homework.

Another option is to do most of Lesson 3.3 from the book and do Investigation 3.3.2 as a demonstration using a single computer and an overhead display device.

Construction Tips

This is a very simple construction. Just make sure students construct segment CD to a random point D on $\overleftrightarrow{AB}$, not point A or point B.

Investigate

1. CD should be greater than the distance from point C to the line.

2. Make sure nothing else is selected when students drag point D. As CD approaches the distance from point C to the line, the segment CD approaches being perpendicular to $\overleftrightarrow{AB}$. This will be confirmed when students construct the perpendicular to $\overleftrightarrow{AB}$ through point C. Distance CD is minimized when point D is at the intersection of $\overleftrightarrow{AB}$ and the perpendicular line.

   Students should come up with the following conjecture: The shortest distance from a point to a line is measured along the perpendicular from the point to the line (C-3: Shortest Distance Conjecture).

Explore More

Because this is such a brief investigation, many students may choose to work on the problem posed in this section. A sketch to model the problem is shown at right. The circle represents the 5-mile radius from the sewage plant. Surprisingly, the optimal location for

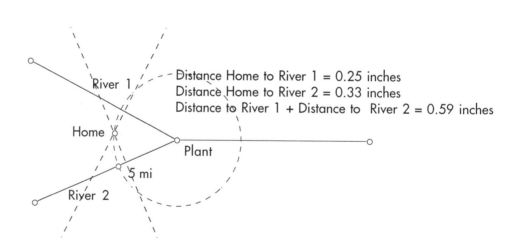

Distance Home to River 1 = 0.25 inches
Distance Home to River 2 = 0.33 inches
Distance to River 1 + Distance to River 2 = 0.59 inches

the house is on one of the banks (assuming you don't mind walking to the other river through the sewage zone).

This becomes obvious when you think of the problem in terms of triangle inequality. Some students will choose not to construct the perpendicular distances but will construct segments from the home to the intersections of the circle with the river, arguing that they don't want to fish in a sewage zone any more than they want to live in it.

Lesson 3.4

Constructing Angle Bisectors

Example Sketches and Scripts

- Angle Bisector Sketch (Mac) or ch03\anglbis.gsp (Windows)

- Angle Bisector Script (Mac) or ch03\anglbis2.gss (Windows)

Discovering Geometry Correlation/Lesson Guide

Lesson 3.4 in *Discovering Geometry* has two more investigations that follow this one. In DG Investigation 3.4.2, students learn to construct an angle bisector using compass and straightedge. In Investigation 3.4.3, students discover that the measure of each angle in an equilateral triangle is 60° (C-5). They use this conjecture in the exercise set to construct angles with measures that are fractions of 60°. If you do Investigation 3.4.1 in the computer lab, you'll need to either take two days for the lesson or assign Investigations 3.4.2 and 3.4.3 in the book along with the homework. Or you could do Investigation 3.4.1 as described here as a demonstration on a single computer with an overhead display device.

Construction Tips

Step 5: Do this the same way you did step 4. Select the point and the ray and choose Distance in the Measure menu.

Investigate

1. The measures of angles *BAD* and *DAC* are equal.

2. If a point is on the bisector of an angle, then it is equally distant from the sides of the angle (C-4: Angle Bisector Conjecture).

Explore More

1. Ray *AC* is the angle bisector of the angle formed by ray *AB* and its reflection.

2. If a point is equally distant from the sides of an angle, then it is on the angle bisector. To demonstrate this, construct an angle and its bisector. Construct a point not on the bisector. Measure the distances from the point to the two sides of the angle. Move the point until those distances are equal. When they are equal, the point will be on the angle bisector.

Lesson 3.7

Constructing Points of Concurrency

Example Sketches and Scripts

- Angle Bisectors (Mac sketch) or ch03\trnglpts\angbis.gsp (Windows sketch)

- Incenter (Mac script) or ch03\incenter.gss (Windows script)

- Perpendicular Bisectors (Mac sketch) or ch03\trnglpts\perpbis.gsp (Windows sketch)

- Circumcenter (Mac script) or ch03\crcmcntr.gss (Windows script)

- Altitudes (Mac sketch) or ch03\trnglpts\altituds.gsp (Windows sketch)

- Orthocenter (Mac script) or ch03\orthcntr.gss (Windows script)

Discovering Geometry Correlation/Lesson Guide

This activity replaces Lesson 3.7 in *Discovering Geometry*. The Geometer's Sketchpad is the ideal medium for the investigations in Lessons 3.7 and 3.8. In *Discovering Geometry,* students investigate all three points of concurrency in Investigation 3.7.1; then they return to the incenter and circumcenter in Investigation 3.7.2. Here, each of the three points of concurrency is fully investigated in a separate investigation.

The three investigations may be too much to get through in a class period. Consider several options, depending on your students' proficiency with Sketchpad and the length of your class period: (1) Have all students do the angle bisectors investigation and then assign each group one or the other of the remaining two investigations. (2) Divide the three investigations among different groups. (3) Have all students start with the first investigation and go as far as they can. Tell them not to worry if they don't finish. In any case, save time at the end of the period to share and, if possible, to demonstrate conjectures so that every student sees them all.

Each investigation has a "Sketch (. . . Continued)" section in which students save a script for a point of concurrency. Doing these sections is a good way to introduce students to scripts and script tools. But skipping them can save time and a potential logistics hassle. In Lesson 3.8, students use the three scripts from Lesson 3.7 and a fourth that they make in Lesson 3.8. To use those scripts as script tools, students will have to have access to a folder containing the four scripts. Even if you do have students make and save scripts, you can avoid trouble by making sure each computer has access to the Triangle Points folder (Mac) or ch03\trnglpts directory (Windows) that comes on the *Discovering Geometry with The Geometer's Sketchpad* disk.

Construction Tips: Angle Bisectors Investigation

Step 3: Select three points, with point *B* the middle selection.

Step 4: Select the two rays and choose Point At Intersection in the Construct menu. Or just click on the intersection with the Selection Arrow tool or the Point tool. If students get ahead of themselves and construct the third angle bisector, they'll have difficulty constructing the point of intersection. Sketchpad doesn't allow a point at the intersection of three objects. Students will need to select two of the three rays and use the Construct menu.

Step 6: The finger of the Text tool needs to be positioned over the label. When it's correctly positioned, a letter "A" appears inside the hand.

Step 8: Where students save their scripts will depend on the setup in your lab. One option is for students to make a folder or directory called something like Triangle Points on their personal floppy disks. That way they'll have access to the scripts regardless of which computer they use in the future.

Investigate

1. The third angle bisector passes through the point of intersection of the first two.

2. Three random lines would intersect in three different points—not in one point. The three angle bisectors of a triangle are concurrent (C-6).

3. The incenter of a triangle is equally distant from the triangle's three sides (C-10).

Construction Tips: Perpendicular Bisectors Investigation

Step 2: It helps if the triangle is acute so that the intersection of the perpendicular bisectors will at least start out inside the triangle.

Step 3: Students can select both segments and construct both midpoints simultaneously by choosing Midpoint in the Construct menu.

Step 5: Use the method described in step 4.

Step 6: Select the two lines and choose Point At Intersection in the Construct menu. Or just click on the intersection with the Selection Arrow tool or the Point tool. If students get ahead of themselves and construct the third perpendicular bisector, they'll have difficulty constructing the point of intersection. Sketchpad doesn't allow a point at the intersection of three objects. Students will need to select two of the three lines and use the Construct menu.

Step 8: Position the finger of the Text tool directly over the label and double-click. Use Ci instead of C to differentiate this point from the centroid, which students construct in Lesson 3.8.

Step 10: Where students save their scripts will depend on the setup in your lab. One option is for students to make a folder or directory called something like Triangle Points on their personal floppy disks. That way they'll have access to the scripts regardless of which computer they use in the future.

Investigate

4. The three perpendicular bisectors of a triangle are concurrent (C-7). For an acute triangle, the point of concurrency falls inside the triangle. For an obtuse triangle, the point of concurrency falls outside the triangle. For a right triangle, the point of concurrency falls at the midpoint of the hypotenuse.

5. The circumcenter of a triangle is equally distant from the triangle's three vertices (C-9).

Construction Tips: Altitudes Investigation

Step 2: It helps if the triangle is acute so that the intersection of the altitudes will at least start out inside the triangle.

Step 4: Use the method described in step 3.

Step 5: Select the two lines and choose Point At Intersection in the Construct menu. Or just click on the intersection with the Selection Arrow tool or the Point tool. If students get ahead of themselves and construct the third altitude line, they'll have difficulty constructing the point of intersection. Sketchpad doesn't allow a point at the intersection of three objects. Students will need to select two of the three lines and use the Construct menu.

Step 7: Position the finger of the Text tool directly over the label and double-click.

Step 9: Where students save their scripts will depend on the setup in your lab. One option is for students to make a folder or directory called something like Triangle Points on their personal floppy disks. That way they'll have access to the scripts regardless of which computer they use in the future.

Investigate

6. The three altitudes of a triangle are concurrent (C-8). For an acute triangle, the point of concurrency falls inside the triangle. For an obtuse triangle, the point of concurrency falls outside the triangle. For a right triangle, the point of concurrency falls at the vertex of the right angle.

Explore More

1. By following these steps, students should be able to construct a triangle and its circumscribed circle. The circumcenter is the center of the circumscribed circle because it is equally distant from the triangle's three vertices.

2. By following these steps, students will draw a circle that is inscribed in the triangle as long as they don't change the triangle. The incenter is the center of the inscribed circle because it is equally distant from the triangle's three sides. To construct an inscribed circle that will stay inscribed, construct a perpendicular from the incenter to any side of the triangle. Then construct the circle to the intersection of this side and the perpendicular.

Lesson 3.8

The Centroid

Example Sketches and Scripts

- Medians (Mac sketch) or ch03\trnglpts\medians.gsp (Windows sketch)
- Centroid (Mac script) or ch03\trnglpts\centroid.gss (Windows script)
- Incenter (Mac script) or ch03\incenter.gss (Windows script)
- Circumcenter (Mac script) or ch03\crcmcntr.gss (Windows script)
- Orthocenter (Mac script) or ch03\orthcntr.gss (Windows script)

Discovering Geometry Correlation/Lesson Guide

This activity replaces Lesson 3.8 in *Discovering Geometry*. The Geometer's Sketchpad is the ideal medium for the investigations in Lessons 3.7 and 3.8.

Investigation 3.8.3 assumes students have done all of Lesson 3.7. They use the three scripts from Lesson 3.7 and a fourth that they make in Lesson 3.8. To use those scripts as script tools, students will have to have access to a folder containing the four scripts. If students didn't do any or all of Lesson 3.7, you can still do Investigation 3.8.3 if you make sure each computer has access to the Triangle Points folder (Mac) or ch03\trnglpts directory (Windows) that comes on the *Discovering Geometry with The Geometer's Sketchpad* disk. Even if students did do Lesson 3.7, it might be easier logistically to make the Triangle Points folder accessible to them.

Construction Tips: Investigation 3.8.1

Step 4: Select the two medians and choose Point At Intersection in the Construct menu. Or just click on the intersection with the Selection Arrow tool or the Point tool. If students get ahead of themselves and construct the median, they'll have difficulty constructing the point of intersection. Sketchpad doesn't allow a point at the intersection of three objects. Students will need to select two of the three segments and use the Construct menu.

Investigate

1. Students should realize that they need to construct a midpoint before they can construct a median. The three medians of a triangle are concurrent (C-11).

Construction Tips: Investigation 3.8.2

Step 5: The finger of the Text tool needs to be positioned over the label. When it's correctly positioned, a letter "A" appears inside the hand. Change the label to *Ce* instead of just *C* to differentiate it from the circumcenter.

Investigate

2. The centroid of a triangle divides each median into two parts so that the distance from the centroid to the vertex is twice the distance from the centroid to the midpoint (C-12). Students can confirm this by using the calculator on these distances.

3. Depending on the order in which students selected measures when they created tables, the points should lie on a line with slope 1/2 or 2. This slope represents the ratio of the two lengths into which the centroid divides each median.

Construction Tips: Investigation 3.8.3

Step 11: Where students save their scripts will depend on the setup in your lab. Have them save this script in the same folder in which they saved the scripts from Lesson 3.7.

Steps 12–21 describe how students can set a script tool folder and use script tools. It might be easiest to demonstrate steps 12–19 on an overhead display and have students follow along.

Investigate

4. The circumcenter, the centroid, and the orthocenter are the three points of concurrency that always lie on the Euler line (C-13).

5. All four points are collinear in isosceles triangles.

6. All four points are coincident in equilateral triangles.

7. The orthocenter and the circumcenter are the endpoints of the Euler segment. The centroid lies between them.

8. The centroid divides the Euler segment into two parts so that the smaller part is half as long as the larger part (C-14).

Lesson 4.1
Discovering Angle Relationships

Example Sketches
- Angle Relationships (Mac) or ch04\angles.gsp (Windows)

Discovering Geometry Correlation/Lesson Guide
This activity covers the same material as Lesson 4.1 in the book, excluding the exercise set. Investigations 4.1.1 and 4.1.2 are combined here.

Construction Tips
Steps 1 and 2: It's best if students construct these lines as instructed so that they share a control point A. This method ensures that the point of intersection A will remain fixed when students move point B or C.

Investigate
1. No matter what you drag, two pairs of angles are always congruent. Students may also notice that a pair of angles that are not congruent add to 180°.

2. If two angles are vertical angles, then they are congruent (C-15: Vertical Angles Conjecture).

3. a. Besides $\angle BAC$ and $\angle CAD$ already given in the example, students should find three more pairs. These are $\angle CAD$ and $\angle DAE$, $\angle DAE$ and $\angle EAB$, $\angle EAB$ and $\angle BAC$.

   b. If two angles are a linear pair of angles, then they are supplementary (C-16: Linear Pair Conjecture).

4. Angles in a linear pair are congruent only when the angles are right angles.

Explore More
These problems are good for students who work through the activity quickly and need an extra challenge. They also review some basic algebra skills.

1. a. When three lines intersect, you can find all six angles if you know the measures of any two nonvertical angles.

   b. The angles are all congruent if and only if each angle measures 60°.

2. a. When four lines intersect, you can find all eight angles if you know the measures of three angles, as long as no two of the angles are a pair of vertical angles.

   b. The angles are all congruent if and only if each angle measures 45°.

3. a. When n lines intersect, you can find all $2n$ angles if you know the measures of $n - 1$ angles, as long as no two of the angles are a pair of vertical angles.

   b. The angles are all congruent if and only if each angle measures 360°/n.

Lesson 4.2

Discovering Properties of Parallel Lines

Example Sketches

- Parallel Lines (Mac) or ch04\parallel.gsp (Windows)

Discovering Geometry Correlation/Lesson Guide

Note that the activity does not include Investigation 4.2.3 from the book, which demonstrates how to construct parallel lines with a compass and straightedge. Assign it for homework along with the exercise set. Students need to know about this investigation before they attempt Exercises 10, 11, and 12. Otherwise, the activity covers the same material as the other investigations in the book. Also, Explore More 3 covers the same concept as Investigation 4.2.3.

Construction Tips: Investigation 4.2.1

Step 3: As students construct the transversal, make sure that the cross hairs for the control points land directly on *A* and *C*. This will ensure that the three lines are attached correctly.

Step 4: Make sure students locate the points as shown, so that their figures correspond to the angles described later.

Investigate

1. Four of the angles are always congruent. The remaining four are also congruent.

2. a. Besides the sample pair ∠*FCE* and ∠*CAB*, there are three more pairs: ∠*ECA* and ∠*BAH*, ∠*ACD* and ∠*HAG*, and ∠*GAC* and ∠*DCF*. Note that there are several correct ways to label each angle.

    b. If two parallel lines are cut by a transversal, then corresponding angles are congruent (C-17a: Corresponding Angle Conjecture).

3. a. Besides the sample pair ∠*ECA* and ∠*CAG*, there is one more pair: ∠*DCA* and ∠*CAB*.

    b. If two parallel lines are cut by a transversal, then alternate interior angles are congruent (C-17b: Alternate Interior Angle Conjecture).

4. a. Besides the sample pair ∠*FCE* and ∠*HAG*, there is one more pair: ∠*DCF* and ∠*BAH*.

    b. If two parallel lines are cut by a transversal, then alternate exterior angles are congruent (C-17c: Alternate Exterior Angle Conjecture).

5. If two parallel lines are cut by a transversal, then corresponding angles are congruent, alternate interior angles are congruent, and alternate exterior angles are congruent (C-17: Parallel Lines Conjecture).

6. Answers may vary. The converse may be hard for students to understand. The purpose of question 6 is to give students a chance to understand the converse and speculate about its truth or falsity before following a set of steps to test it on the computer.

Construction Tips: Investigation 4.2.2

Steps 1 and 2: Students can construct these lines any way they want, as long as there are enough points to measure all eight angles and as long as the points of intersection are properly constructed to be on two lines simultaneously.

Step 3: It might be difficult to get the angle measurements to match exactly, especially if the measurements are very precise. To make this step easier, you could change the measurements to a rougher precision using Preferences from the Display menu.

Investigate

7. If two lines are cut by a transversal to form pairs of congruent corresponding angles, congruent alternate interior angles, and congruent alternate exterior angles, then the lines are parallel (C-18: Converse of the Parallel Lines Conjecture).

Explore More

1. Students should find two pairs of consecutive interior angles. Their names will vary, depending on the labels in the sketch. A sample conjecture would be: If parallel lines are cut by a transversal, then consecutive interior angles are supplementary.

2. Students should find two pairs of consecutive exterior angles. Their names will vary, depending on the labels in the sketch. A sample conjecture would be: If parallel lines are cut by a transversal, then consecutive exterior angles are supplementary.

3. If students mark the angle and the center of rotation properly, they should be able to rotate $\overleftrightarrow{CA}$ by the marked angle to get it parallel to $\overleftrightarrow{AB}$. You can use the Converse of the Parallel Lines Conjecture to conclude that lines constructed in this manner must be parallel.

   The argument goes like this: The construction guarantees that a pair of corresponding angles are congruent. If one pair of corresponding angles are congruent, you can use the Vertical Angles Conjecture and the Linear Pair Conjecture to show that every other pair of corresponding angles and every pair of alternate interior and alternate exterior angles are also congruent. Once you have shown all these pairs to be congruent, you can use the Converse of the Parallel Lines Conjecture to conclude that the lines are parallel. Clearly, you might not expect this much deductive rigor from every student. You should probably be satisfied if they can explain how they are using the converse in this construction.

Lesson 4.3

Midpoint and Slope Conjectures

Required Sketches

- Slope of a Line (Mac) or ch04\slopelin.gsp (Windows)

Discovering Geometry Correlation/Lesson Guide

This activity is essentially four investigations. All of them together could replace the investigations in Lesson 4.3 in the book. The first investigation explores the Midpoint Conjecture, and the rest of the investigations explore the slope of a line. Investigation 4.3.2 has three parts. Sketch A is a brief introduction to slope that allows students to develop or review an intuitive connection between the slope of a line and the appearance of the line. This also prepares them for Sketch B: Playing the Slope Game, which gives them a fun way to test their knowledge of slope. Finally, Sketch C develops a method for calculating the slope of a line using a pair of coordinate points on the line. This leads to the Slope of a Line Conjecture.

It is probably impossible to do all four investigations in one class period. If you decide to spend two days on this lesson, you might break up the lesson this way:

Day 1: Investigation 4.3.1: The midpoint Conjecture and Investigation 4.3.2 Sketch A. Assign problems 1–8, 10, 11, 38, and 39 from the exercise set.

Day 2: Investigation 4.3.2 Sketch B: Playing the Slope Game and Investigation 4.3.2 Sketch C: Calculating the Slope of a Line. Assign the remaining problems from the exercise set.

Of course, you can also pick only some of these computer activities and use the text for any missing concepts. Your students have probably studied slope in a previous class, so the work with slope should move quickly if it is review. The same may be true for the midpoint conjecture.

Construction Tips: Investigation 4.3.1

Step 4: If students select all three points first, they can measure all three coordinates at the same time.

Investigate

1. The x-coordinate of the midpoint is always exactly in between the x-coordinates of the endpoints. The same is true for the y-coordinate. You may want to encourage students to use the word *average*. Students might have trouble seeing the pattern if the coordinate values are precise to many decimal places. To change the precision, use Preferences in the Display menu.

2. If (x_1, y_1) and (x_2, y_2) are the coordinates of the endpoints of a segment, then the coordinates of the midpoint are $\left(\frac{x_1+x_2}{2}, \frac{y_1+y_2}{2}\right)$ (C-19: Coordinate Midpoint Conjecture).

3. Answers will vary. This problem gives students a chance to check their conjecture on numbers that are not integers. The conjecture holds for any real numbers, not just integers.

Construction Tips: Investigation 4.3.2 Sketch A

This is a very simple construction.

Investigate

4. Lines going "downhill" from left to right have negative slope. Lines going "uphill" from left to right have positive slope.

5. A horizontal line has a slope of zero.

6. If you ignore the sign of the slope measurement, a larger value indicates a steeper slope. This might be a good time to review absolute value, since the absolute value of the slope measurement is always larger for steeper slopes.

7. The slope of a vertical line is undefined.

Construction Tips: Investigation 4.3.2 Sketch B

You can use the sample sketch The Slope Game (Mac) or ch04\slopegam.gsp (Windows) to replace this construction.

Step 1: It is very important that no labels are showing. To turn off a label, click the labeled object with the Text tool. Also, you can change which labels show up automatically in the Preferences menu under Display. Students may prefer not to have any labels showing up automatically, especially for this game.

Investigate

8. Students often have perfect scores, which helps build their confidence. Have students play this game for a few rounds. If you wish, have them record their scores on the board after a certain number of rounds. This is an easy way for you to check on how they are doing.

Construction Tips: Investigation 4.3.2 Sketch C

Step 2: This step may be a hard one for students, and they might need some hints. Remind them that the x-coordinate records the vertical positioning of a point. It's important that they don't measure the vertical side of the right triangle, because this measurement will not represent the change from D to A if that change is negative.

Step 4: Make sure students select the measurements themselves to put in the calculator and don't type in the numbers that happen to be on the screen at the time.

Investigate

9. The ratio *rise/run* remains unchanged for these different triangles.

10. The ratio *rise/run* is zero for a horizontal line.

11. The ratio *rise/run* is undefined. The measurement may show up as the infinity symbol.

12. When the ratio *rise/run* is negative, the line slopes "downhill" from left to right.

13. The slope of the line matches the ratio *rise/run*, so to calculate slope find the rise and run between a pair of points and calculate the ratio of these two numbers.

14. The slope m of a line (or segment) through P_1 and P_2 with coordinates (x_1, y_1) and
    (x_2, y_2) where $x_1 \neq x_2$ is $m = \dfrac{y_2 - y_1}{x_2 - x_1}$ (C-20: Slope of a Line Conjecture).

Explore More

1. a. This problem gives students a chance to check the Midpoint Conjecture using Sketchpad. The hint in the student text for selecting the y-coordinate and x-coordinate only is important, since this part of the construction can be confusing.

    b. Now students check their results of the Slope of a Line Conjecture. Again, the hint in the text should be helpful, since the calculator can be tricky to use for more complicated calculations. Students should use the Remove button in the calculator when they make mistakes.

Lesson 4.4

Slopes of Parallel and Perpendicular Lines

Example Sketches

• Parallel/Perp Slopes (Mac) or ch04\paraslope.gsp (Windows)

Discovering Geometry Correlation/Lesson Guide

This activity covers the same content as the investigations in the student text, although there are a few differences in presentation. The approach here does not use the coordinate plane. Also, for C-22: Perpendicular Slope Conjecture, students using this activity will probably not write a conjecture about the slopes of perpendicular lines that includes the term "negative reciprocal," as expected in the text. They will simply observe that the product of the slopes of perpendicular lines is −1. You may want to spend some time discussing why this conjecture means the same as the one in the text and reviewing the term "negative reciprocal."

Construction Tips: Investigation 4.4.1

Step 1: There are many ways to construct the point of intersection. You can carefully place a point at that spot (drag the lines to make sure the point is anchored correctly), you can click on the spot with the Selection Arrow tool, or you can select both lines and choose Point of Intersection from the Construct menu.

Step 2: To measure an angle, select three points on the angle, making sure the middle point is the vertex.

Investigate

1. If two lines have equal slopes, then they are parallel.

2. If two lines are parallel, then they have equal slopes.

3. Two lines are parallel if and only if their slopes are equal (C-21: Parallel Slope Conjecture).

Construction Tips: Investigation 4.4.3

Step 3: To construct a perpendicular to a line through a point, select the line and the point and choose Perpendicular Line from the Construct menu.

Investigate

4. If two lines are perpendicular, then the product of their slopes is −1.

5. If two lines have slopes whose product is −1, then the lines must be perpendicular.

6. Two lines are perpendicular if and only if their slopes have a product of −1 (C-22: Perpendicular Slope Conjecture, with different wording).

Lesson 4.5

Equations of Lines

Example Sketches

- Equation of a Line (Mac) or ch04\linequa.gsp (Windows)
- Slope-Intercept Form (Mac) or ch04\slopeint.gsp (Windows)

Discovering Geometry Correlation/Lesson Guide

This activity covers the same material as the investigations in the student text. The student text does contain more examples that demonstrate how to find the equation of a line using calculations starting with the coordinates of two points on the line. You might suggest that students read these examples before starting the exercises.

Investigate

1. Students should observe that m is the slope of the line and b is the y-coordinate of its y-intercept.

2. Answers may vary. This is a chance for students to test their observations from the preceding question.

3. Give students time to play with this. It is easier to estimate both the slope and the y-intercept if Snap to Grid is on. If Snap to Grid is off, close estimates for equations are fine.

Explore More

1. This problem is identical to Take Another Look 4.5, problem 2.

   Such a pair of parallel lines will be two units apart only when the lines are horizontal with slope of zero. As you increase the slope of the lines, the distance between them decreases, and when the lines are vertical they are also coincident, since the distance between them has diminished to zero.

   Here is one possible sequence of steps to construct a set of parallel lines with y-intercepts two units apart:

   Draw a line and construct the point where it intersects the y-axis. Translate this point up two units using the Transform menu. Then construct a line parallel to the first line through this image point.
   Warning: The units used in the translation need to match the units of the grid. This will be true as long as the grid retains its original scale. The only way to scale the grid is to drag the point (1, 0). To avoid scaling the grid accidentally, you can always hide this point.

2. Answers will vary. The computer's rounding of fractions can make a difference. For example, Sketchpad measured the same line in standard form and in slope-intercept form and produced these two equations:

   $0.333x + 0.167y = 0.500$

   $y = -2.00x + 3.00$

   It is impossible to transform one equation exactly into the other. The second equation turns into
   $\frac{1}{3}x + \frac{1}{6}y = \frac{1}{2}$
   The fractional coefficients of this equation round to the coefficients of the first equation.

Lesson 5.1

Triangle Sum Conjecture

Example Sketches

• Triangle Sum (Mac) or ch05\trisum.gsp (Windows)

Discovering Geometry Correlation/Lesson Guide

Use this lesson in place of, or as an extension to, Lesson 5.1 in *Discovering Geometry*. This lesson covers only Investigation 5.1.1. If you replace *DG* Lesson 5.1 with this one, do Investigation 5.1.2 as a follow-along demonstration or assign it as homework.

Investigate

1. The sum is always 180°.

2. The sum of the measures of the angles in a triangle is 180° (C-25: Triangle Sum Conjecture).

Explore More

1. a. Students should notice that the three angles are congruent to the three angles of the triangle.

    b. Answers will vary. Line *ED* // $\overline{AB}$; therefore, $\angle ACD \cong \angle BAC$ and $\angle BCE \cong \angle ABC$ by AIA. The sum of $m\angle ACD + m\angle BCA + m\angle BCE = 180° = m\angle CAB + m\angle BCA + m\angle ABC$.

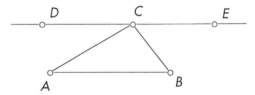

2. a. A third congruent triangle will fill the space between the two triangles.

    b. The three angles are the three angles of the triangle, and the three angles form a straight line.

    c. This confirms the Triangle Sum Conjecture by demonstrating that the three angles of the triangle form a straight line and thus sum to 180°.

3. Answers will vary. See Lesson 6.1: Polygon Sum Conjecture.

4. Answers will vary.

Lesson 5.2

Discovering Properties of Isosceles Triangles

Example Sketches

- Isosceles Δ (Mac) or ch05\isotri.gsp (Windows)
- Δ Base Angles (Mac) or ch05\baseangl.gsp (Windows)

Discovering Geometry Correlation/Lesson Guide

Use this activity in place of, or as an extension to, Lesson 5.2 in *Discovering Geometry*. This activity covers C-27 and
C-28. Students should read the proof in the text (p. 234) for C-29 or do the Explore More activity on equilateral triangles.

Construction Tips

You may want to have students make an isosceles triangle script.

Investigate

1. The triangle is always isosceles because two of the sides are radii of the same circle.

2. The measures of the two angles are always equal.

3. If a triangle is isosceles, then its base angles are congruent (C-27: Isosceles Triangle Conjecture).

4. Students should observe that the triangle appears isosceles.

5. The lengths of $\overline{BD}$ and $\overline{AD}$ are equal.

6. If a triangle has two congruent angles, then it is an isosceles triangle (C-28: Converse of the Isosceles Triangle Conjecture).

Explore More

1. An equilateral triangle is equiangular, and, conversely, an equiangular triangle is equilateral (C-29: Equilateral Triangle Conjecture).

2. Refer to the figure below. Angle *A* is the angle with the greatest measure.

   Use the following steps to divide a triangle into a kite and two isosceles triangles: Draw Δ*ABC*. Construct altitude *AD*. Construct the midpoint *E* of $\overline{AB}$ and the midpoint *F* of $\overline{AC}$. Connect points *A, F, D,* and *E* to form a kite.

   Student work should show that this divides the triangle into two isosceles triangles and a kite.

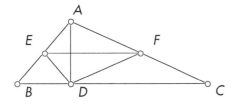

3. Answers will vary. When a triangle is constructed such that the measure of one acute angle is half the measure of the other acute angle, the triangle can be divided into two isosceles triangles, as shown below.

   m∠ABD = 54°
   m∠ADB = 27°

   AB = 2.32 cm
   AC = 2.32 cm
   CD = 2.32 cm

Lesson 5.3

Triangle Inequalities

Example Sketches

- Δ Inequality (Mac) or ch05\triineq.gsp (Windows)

- Δ Exterior Angle (Mac) or ch05\triextang.gsp (Windows)

Discovering Geometry Correlation/Lesson Guide

Use this lesson in place of, or as an extension to, Lesson 5.3 in *Discovering Geometry*. Cover the definition for remote interior angles, adjacent interior angles, and exterior angles. See page 238 of the student text. Students will need to know these terms to do Investigation 5.3.3.

Investigate

1. Students should notice that the three segments no longer form a triangle when the sum of the lengths of any two segments is less than or equal to the length of the third side.

2. No, it is not possible for the sum of the lengths of any two sides of a triangle to be less than the length of the third side. If the sum of two sides is shorter than the third side, it is impossible for the two ends to connect.

3. The sum of the lengths of any two sides of a triangle is greater than the length of the third side (C-30: Triangle Inequality Conjecture).

4.

AB longest side	Greatest angle? ∠C	AC longest side	Greatest angle? ∠B	BC longest side	Greatest angle? ∠A
AB shortest side	Least angle? ∠C	AC shortest side	Least angle? ∠B	BC shortest side	Least angle? ∠A

5. In a triangle, the longest side is opposite the angle with greatest measure and the shortest side is opposite the angle with least measure (C-31: Side-Angle Inequality Conjecture).

6. The measure of an exterior angle of a triangle is equal to the sum of the measures of the remote interior angles (C-32: Triangle Exterior Angle Conjecture).

Explore More

1. Students should discover that you can form a quadrilateral only if the sum of the lengths of any three segments is greater than the length of the fourth segment.

2. Answers will vary.

Lesson 5.4

SSS, SAS, and SSA Congruence Shortcuts?

Required Sketches

- SSS (Mac) or ch05\sss.gsp (Windows)
- SAS (Mac) or ch05\sas.gsp (Windows)
- SSA (Mac) or ch05\ssa.gsp (Windows)

Discovering Geometry Correlation/Lesson Guide

Use this lesson in place of, or as an extension to, Lesson 5.4 in *Discovering Geometry*. Each investigation is on a separate page so that you can assign a different investigation to each group as suggested in the student text. Some students may make the triangle on the right into a reflection of the triangle on the left. They can either print out the triangle to check or use Sketchpad to measure the three angles to confirm that the two triangles are congruent.

Construction Tips

Students use a premade sketch for these investigations.

Investigate

1. No, you cannot make two triangles that are not congruent.
2. Yes, this is a congruence shortcut.
3. If the three sides of one triangle are congruent to the three sides of another triangle, then the triangles are congruent (C-33: SSS Congruence Conjecture).
4. No, you cannot make two triangles that are not congruent.
5. Yes, this is a congruence shortcut.
6. If two sides and the angle between them in one triangle are congruent to two sides and the angle between them in another triangle, then the triangles are congruent (C-34: SAS Congruence Conjecture).
7. Yes, you can make two triangles that are not congruent.
8. No, this is not a congruence shortcut.
9. If two sides and an angle that is not between the two sides in one triangle are congruent to the corresponding two sides and an angle that is not between the two sides in another triangle, then the two triangles are not necessarily congruent.

Lesson 5.5

ASA, SAA, and AAA Congruence Shortcuts?

Required Sketches

- ASA (Mac) or ch05\asa.gsp (Windows)

- AAA (Mac) or ch05\aaa.gsp (Windows)

Discovering Geometry Correlation/Lesson Guide

Use this lesson in place of, or as an extension to, Lesson 5.5 in *Discovering Geometry*. There is no investigation for SAA. You might ask students to do a Sketchpad construction or remind them of the Third Angle Conjecture. Each investigation is on a separate page so that you can assign a different investigation to each group as suggested in the student text. Some students may make the triangle on the right into a reflection of the triangle on the left. They can either print out the two triangles to check for congruence or use Sketchpad to measure the three sides to confirm that the two triangles are congruent.

Construction Tips

Students use a premade sketch for these investigations.

Investigate

1. No, you cannot make two triangles that are not congruent.

2. Yes, this is a congruence shortcut.

3. If two angles and the side between them in one triangle are congruent to two angles and the side between them in another triangle, then the triangles are congruent (C-35: ASA Congruence Conjecture).

4. Yes, you can make two triangles that are not congruent.

5. No, this is not a congruence shortcut.

6. If the three angles of one triangle are congruent to the three angles of another triangle, then the two triangles are not necessarily congruent.

Lesson 5.7

Isosceles Triangles Revisited

Example Sketches

- Iso Δ Segments (Mac) or ch05\isosegs.gsp
- Iso Δ Segments 2 (Mac) or ch05\isosegs2.gsp

Discovering Geometry Correlation/Lesson Guide

Use this lesson in place of, or as an extension to, Lesson 5.7 in *Discovering Geometry*.

Investigate

1. Segment *AD* is the altitude of the vertex angle.
2. Point *D* is the midpoint of $\overline{CB}$.
3. Segment *AD* is the median of the vertex angle.
4. In an isosceles triangle, the bisector of the vertex angle is also the altitude to the base and the median to the base
    (C-37: Vertex Angle Bisector Conjecture).

Explore More

1. If the bisector of the vertex angle is also the altitude to the base and the median to the base, then the triangle is an isosceles triangle.
2. The triangle is equilateral when the angle bisector, median, and altitude of a nonvertex angle are concurrent.

Lesson 6.1

Polygon Sum Conjecture

Example Sketches

Polygon Sum (Mac) or ch06\polysum.gsp (Windows)

Discovering Geometry Correlation/Lesson Guide

You can use this activity to replace Lesson 6.1 in the text. Explore More 1 and 2 replace Take Another Look 3.

Investigate

1. The angle stays constant at 360° for convex quadrilaterals. For concave quadrilaterals, the angle sum appears to be less than 360° because Sketchpad does not measure angles greater than 180°. (Adventurous students may even discover "crossed polygons," which have sides that cross. Their angle sums also have different rules.)

   The sum of the measures of the four angles of every quadrilateral is 360° (C-38: Quadrilateral Sum Conjecture).

   The text states on page 98 that it will always mean convex polygons when it uses the term polygon. So students can make a general conjecture about polygons without worrying about the concave cases.

2. a. Answers can vary. You might want to organize the polygon selection to make sure that different groups cover different polygons.

   b. Answers will vary. Students could choose a polygon (such as an 11-gon) that does not have a particular name of its own.

3. Answers will vary. Give students time to figure out their prediction. There are a few ways to reason through this problem that might bring them to the correct solution.

4. Answers will vary. Hopefully, students will find that their predictions matched their discoveries. Again, they need to treat the cases of the concave polygons separately. For now, they do not need to worry about them.

5. The sum of the measures of the n angles of an n-gon is $180° (n - 2)$ (C-39: Polygon Sum Conjecture).

   It might be helpful to have groups record their results on the board so that students can observe the different results from around the class. If students need hints, help them notice that the sums go up by 180° for every new side. Since you can't make a polygon with only one side or only two sides, you don't get the first 180° until you have three sides. For this reason, you have to subtract 2 from n before you multiply it by 180°.

Explore More

1. There are a few ways to explain this. Here is one example. Every time you draw a new dashed segment, you create a triangle, except that the last segment creates two triangles. Since you can draw a dashed segment to every vertex except the original vertex and its two neighbors, you draw $n - 3$ dashed segments for every n-gon. This will create
   $n - 3 + 1$, or $n - 2$, new triangles, because of the extra triangle you get at the end. Each triangle has an angle sum
   of 180°, and their angles together make up the angles of the polygon. So the total angle sum of the polygon is
   $(n - 2)180°$.

2. If you consider the caved-in angles as having measures greater than 180°, the Polygon Sum Conjecture still holds. You can still divide a concave polygon into $n - 2$ triangles by drawing diagonals. To test the Polygon Sum Conjecture with Sketchpad, students could calculate (360° – the angle measure) for any caved-in angles and use this calculation when they sum all the angle measures.

3. The sum of the angle measures in an octagon is $(8 - 2)180° = 1080°$. Since a regular octagon has all equal angles, each angle must be one-eighth of this total, or 135°. If you rotate a segment around its endpoint by 135° and continue this process six more times, you should get a regular octagon.

Lesson 6.2

Exterior Angles of a Polygon

Example Sketches

• Polygon Ext Ang (Mac) or ch06\extang.gsp (Windows)

Discovering Geometry Correlation/Lesson Guide

You can use this activity to replace Lesson 6.2 in the text. Explore More 1 replaces Take Another Look 3. This activity extends the meaning of C-41, the Equiangular Polygon Conjecture, by having students construct regular polygons.

Construction Tips: Investigation 6.2A

Step 3: Make sure that students measure the exterior angles, not the interior angles, and that they measure them all.

Investigate

1. In any polygon, the sum of the exterior angles will be 360°. This sum will appear to change only if the polygon is concave. This is because Sketchpad does not measure angles with measures greater than 180°.

2. The sum of the measures of one set of exterior angles is 360° (C-40: Exterior Angle Sum Conjecture).

3. Answers will vary depending on the polygon. An equiangular hexagon has 120° interior angles. An equiangular heptagon has 128 $\frac{4}{7}$°, or roughly 128.57°, interior angles. An equiangular octagon has 135° interior angles. Students' methods for finding these measures will vary (see the answer to question 4 below).

Construction Tips: Investigation 6.2B

Step 3: Make sure students rotate the endpoints of the segment as well as the segment itself.

Step 4: One way to finish this construction is to continue rotating successive segments around successive centers until you arrive back at the starting segment again. Students might also use reflections and translations, depending on the symmetry of their particular polygon.

Investigate

4. Give students time to figure out this formula. The measure of each angle of a regular n-gon can be found by using either of the following formulas: $(n - 2)180°/n$ or $180° - 360°/n$. The first formula is the sum of the interior angles divided by the number of angles. To derive the second formula, start with a linear pair and subtract the exterior angle to get the interior angle.

5. Probably every equiangular polygon students constructed was also equilateral.

6. There are many such examples. The simplest one is a rectangle that is not a square, since it has four equal right angles but sides of different lengths. Any polygon with more than three sides can be equiangular without being equilateral. One way to visualize this is to take a regular polygon and stretch it in such a way that you elongate some sides but leave the angles unchanged.

Explore More

1. Encourage all students to try this. It's easy to do, and it's a dazzling demonstration that the sum of these angles is 360°. As you dilate the figure toward any point, the polygon will shrink toward that point, leaving you with only the angles going all the way around a common vertex. You'll want to discuss the fact that when you dilate a polygon the measures of the angles remain constant. You can measure the exterior angles before you dilate, and students will see that the angle measures don't change.

2. The simplest such example is a rectangle, although you might challenge students to construct a polygon with more sides. There are many ways to construct a rectangle. Here is one interesting way that can be generalized for constructing any equiangular polygon by changing the angle of rotation: Start with a line, and mark one of the control points on the line as a center of rotation. Rotate the line 90° and then construct a free point on the new line. Mark this new free point as a center of rotation and rotate the new line by 90°. Continue this process until the newest line intersects the original line.

Lesson 6.3

Discovering Kite and Trapezoid Properties

Required Sketches

• Quad Family (Mac) or ch06\quadfmly.gsp (Windows)

Discovering Geometry Correlation/Lesson Guide

This activity replaces Lesson 6.3 and follows the same steps as the student text. Explore More 4 replaces Take Another Look 4.

Construction Tips: Investigation 6.3.1

Step 1: If your students need an extra challenge, have them construct their own kite instead of finding it in the prepared sketch. A simple way to construct a kite is to reflect a triangle across one of its sides. Notice that both this construction and the construction in the prepared sketch result in kites that can be manipulated into rhombuses or "darts" (concave kites), in which case they no longer satisfy the *Discovering Geometry* definition of a kite.

Step 3: To construct the point of intersection, click on that spot with either the Selection Arrow tool or the Point tool. Also, you can select both segments and choose Point at Intersection from the Construct menu.

Investigate

You might want to point out to students at the end of this investigation that kite properties hold for rhombuses as well.

1. The diagonals of a kite are perpendicular (C-42: Kite Diagonals Conjecture).

2. The diagonal connecting the vertex angles of a kite is the perpendicular bisector of the other diagonal (C-43: Kite Diagonal Bisector Conjecture). Encourage students to measure the four distances from the intersection point of the diagonals to the vertices to confirm this.

3. The nonvertex angles of a kite are congruent (C-44: Kite Angles Conjecture).

4. The vertex angles of a kite are bisected by a diagonal (C-45: Kite Angle Bisector Conjecture). Encourage students to measure the smaller angles formed by the diagonals to confirm this.

Construction Tips: Investigation 6.3.2

Step 1: If your students need an extra challenge, have them construct their own trapezoid instead of finding it in the prepared sketch. To construct a trapezoid, create a line parallel to a segment and connect the line to the segment with two more segments. Then hide the line and replace it with a segment. Both this construction and the construction in the prepared sketch result in trapezoids that can be manipulated into parallelograms, in which case they no longer satisfy the *Discovering Geometry* definition of a trapezoid.

Investigate

5. The consecutive angles between the bases of a trapezoid are supplementary (C-46: Trapezoid Consecutive Angles Conjecture).

Construction Tips: Investigation 6.3.3

Step 1: If your students need an extra challenge, have them construct their own isosceles trapezoid instead of finding it in the prepared sketch. Perhaps the simplest way is to use reflections. Construct a segment and then a mirror line next to the segment. Reflect the segment across the mirror line and finish the isosceles trapezoid by connecting the appropriate vertices. Both this construction and the construction in the prepared sketch result in isosceles trapezoids that can be manipulated into rectangles, in which case they no longer satisfy the *Discovering Geometry* definition of a trapezoid.

Investigate

You might want to point out to students at the end of this investigation that isosceles trapezoid properties hold for rectangles as well.

6. The base angles of an isosceles trapezoid are congruent (C-47: Isosceles Trapezoid Conjecture).

7. The diagonals of an isosceles trapezoid are congruent (C-48: Isosceles Trapezoid Diagonals Conjecture).

Explore More

Note on Explore More 1–3: It might be both fun and useful to save these polygons as script tools. To do this, select the polygon and choose Make Script from the Work menu. Save this new script, using the name of the polygon, into the appropriate folder where you plan to keep script tools. This folder might be on a server, or it might be on the student's disk. If this folder is not already selected for text tools, follow this procedure: In the Display menu, choose Preferences. In this menu choose More, and in the next menu choose Set (you may first have to choose Clear). Now find your script tools folder and make sure it appears in the name of the long button at the bottom of the dialog box. Click this long button and click Continue and then OK to get back to your home screen. A double-arrow symbol should appear at the bottom of your toolbar. Click this symbol, select your new tool, and try it out.

1. A simple way to construct a kite is to reflect a triangle across one of its sides. Notice that both this construction and the construction in the prepared sketch result in kites that can be manipulated into rhombuses or "darts" (concave kites), in which case they no longer satisfy the *Discovering Geometry* definition of a kite.

2. To construct a trapezoid, create a line parallel to a segment and connect the line to the segment with two more segments. Then hide the line and replace it with a segment. Both this construction and the construction in the prepared sketch result in trapezoids that can be manipulated into parallelograms, in which case they no longer satisfy the *Discovering Geometry* definition of a trapezoid.

3. Perhaps the simplest way to construct an isosceles trapezoid is to use reflections. Construct a segment and then a mirror line next to the segment. Reflect the segment across the mirror line and finish the isosceles trapezoid by connecting the appropriate vertices. Both this construction and the construction in the prepared sketch result in isosceles trapezoids that can be manipulated into rectangles, in which case they no longer satisfy the *Discovering Geometry* definition of a trapezoid.

4. If you extend the diagonals of the darts so that they always intersect, then all the kite conjectures still hold.

Lesson 6.4

Discovering Properties of Midsegments

Required Sketches

• Quad Family (Mac) or ch06\quadfmly.gsp (Windows)

Discovering Geometry Correlation/Lesson Guide

This activity replaces Lesson 6.4 in the text.

Investigate

1. The three midsegments of a triangle divide the triangle into four congruent triangles (C-49). Encourage students to measure angles and sides to verify that the triangles are congruent. This might be a good time to review the triangle congruency conjectures: Have students figure out a minimal group of sides and angles that would be sufficient to conclude that all four triangles are congruent. (For example, they could measure two pairs of corresponding sides and the included angle on each triangle and use the SAS Congruence Conjecture.)

2. Answers may vary. Give students a chance to notice any of the properties before measuring. They may see that the length of the midsegment must be half that of the third side and also that the two are parallel.

3. A midsegment of a triangle is parallel to the third side and half the length of the third side (C-50: Triangle Midsegment Conjecture).

Construction Tips: Investigation 6.4.2

Step 1: If your students need an extra challenge, have them construct their own trapezoid instead of finding it in the prepared sketch. To construct a trapezoid, create a line parallel to a segment and connect the line to the segment with two more segments. Then hide the line and replace it with a segment. Both this construction and the construction in the prepared sketch result in trapezoids that can be manipulated into parallelograms, in which case they no longer satisfy the *Discovering Geometry* definition of a trapezoid.

Step 2: Select the pair of nonparallel sides and choose Point at Midpoint in the Construct menu. Then connect these two midpoints.

Investigate

4. The midsegment of a trapezoid is parallel to the bases.

5. The midsegment of a trapezoid is equal in length to the average of the lengths of the bases. Encourage students to calculate the average of the lengths of the bases using the calculator.

6. The midsegment of a trapezoid is parallel to the bases and equal in length to the average of the two base lengths
(C-51: Trapezoid Midsegment Conjecture).

Lesson 6.5
Discovering Properties of Parallelograms

Example Sketches

• Parallelogram Properties (Mac) or ch06\paraprop.gsp (Windows)

Discovering Geometry Correlation/Lesson Guide

This activity replaces Lesson 6.5.

Construction Tips

Step 5: To construct a point of intersection, click at that spot with either the Selection Arrow tool or the Point tool. Also, you can select both lines and choose Point At Intersection in the Construct menu.

Investigate

1. The opposite angles of a parallelogram are congruent (C-52).

2. The consecutive angles of a parallelogram are supplementary (C-53).

3. The opposite sides of a parallelogram are congruent (C-54).

4. The diagonals of a parallelogram bisect each other (C-55).

Explore More

Here is a construction method that relies on the fact that the diagonals of a rectangle bisect each other. Draw a segment and find its midpoint. (This will be the first diagonal.) Draw another segment with the midpoint as one of its endpoints. Mark the midpoint as a center and rotate this second segment by 180°. Now you have the second diagonal. Connect the endpoints of the diagonals to create the parallelogram.

It might be both fun and useful to save the parallelogram as a Script tool. To do this, select the parallelogram and choose Make Script from the Work menu. Save this new script as Parallelogram into the appropriate folder where you plan to keep script tools. This folder might be on a server, or it might be on the student's disk. If this folder is not already selected for text tools, follow this procedure: In the Display menu, choose Preferences. In this menu choose More, and in the next menu choose Set (you may first have to choose Clear). Now find your script tools folder and make sure it appears in the name of the long button at the bottom of the dialog box. Click this long button and click Continue and then OK to get back to your home screen. A double-arrow symbol should appear at the bottom of your toolbar. Click this symbol, select your new tool, and try it out.

Lesson 6.6

Discovering Properties of Special Parallelograms

Required Sketches

• Quad Family (Mac) or ch06\quadfmly.gsp (Windows)

Discovering Geometry Correlation/Lesson Guide

This activity replaces Lesson 6.6. The only part of the lesson not covered here is Investigation 6.6.1, in which students learn a specific method of constructing a rhombus. You can replace this investigation with Explore More 1, except that here students must find their own method to construct a rhombus and may not necessarily use the one from the text. Explore More 4 is the same as Take Another Look 4.

Construction Tips: Investigation 6.6.2

Step 1: If your students need an extra challenge, have them construct their own rhombus instead of finding it in the prepared sketch. Here is one way to construct a rhombus: Construct a circle AB and construct a radius from A to B as well as another radial segment AC. Now construct circles CA and BA and find their point of intersection. Finish your rhombus by constructing the remaining sides.

Step 3: To construct a point of intersection, click at that spot with the Selection Arrow tool or the Point tool. Also, you can select both lines and choose Point at Intersection in the Construct menu.

Investigate

1. The diagonals of a rhombus are perpendicular bisectors of each other (C-57). Encourage students to measure an angle formed by the diagonals to verify that it measures 90°. Also encourage them to measure the four distances from the intersection point of the diagonals to the vertices. To measure distances between a pair of points, select both points and choose Distance in the Measure menu.

2. The diagonals of a rhombus bisect the angles of the rhombus (C-58). Encourage students to measure the smaller angles formed at each vertex to verify that each pair has equal measure.

Construction Tips: Investigation 6.6.3A

Step 1: If your students need an extra challenge, have them construct their own rectangle instead of finding it in the prepared sketch. Here is one way to construct a rectangle: Construct a segment. Select the segment and both endpoints and choose Perpendicular Line from the Construct menu. Construct a free point on one of the lines. Select this new point and the original segment and choose Parallel Line in the Construct menu. Construct the last remaining vertex of the rectangle, hide all the lines, and replace them with segments.

Investigate

3. The measure of each angle of a rectangle is 90° (C-59).

4. The diagonals of a rectangle are congruent (C-60). Encourage students to measure both diagonals.

Construction Tips: Investigation 6.6.3B

If your students need an extra challenge, have them construct their own square instead of finding it in the prepared sketch. Here is a way to construct a square that makes use of the properties of both a rectangle and a rhombus: Construct a segment and its midpoint. Mark the midpoint as a center. Select the segment and its endpoints and rotate the segment by 90°. You have just created the diagonals of a square. Connect the endpoints to create the square.

Investigate

5. Every conjecture that holds for a rectangle or a rhombus also holds for a square, since a square is a rectangular rhombus.

6. a. A square is an equiangular rhombus.

   b. A square is an equilateral rectangle.

Explore More

Note on Explore More 1–3: It might be both fun and useful to save these polygons as script tools. To do this, select the polygon and choose Make Script from the Work menu. Save this new script, using the name of the polygon, into the appropriate folder where you plan to keep script tools. This folder might be on a server, or it might be on the student's disk. If this folder is not already selected for text tools, follow this procedure: In the Display menu, choose Preferences. In this menu choose More, and in the next menu choose Set (you may first have to choose Clear). Now find your script tools folder and make sure it appears in the name of the long button at the bottom of the dialog box. Click this long button and click Continue and then OK to get back to your home screen. A double-arrow symbol should appear at the bottom of your toolbar. Click this symbol, select your new tool, and try it out.

1. There are many ways to construct a rhombus. Here is one: Construct a circle *AB* and construct a radius from *A* to *B* as well as another radial segment *AC*. Now construct circles *CA* and *BA* and find their point of intersection. Finish your rhombus by constructing the remaining sides.

2. There are many ways to construct a rectangle. Here is one: Construct a segment. Select the segment and both endpoints and choose Perpendicular Line from the Construct menu. Construct a free point on one of the lines. Select this new point and the original segment and choose Parallel Line in the Construct menu. Construct the last remaining vertex of the rectangle, hide all the lines, and replace them with segments.

3. There are many ways to construct a square. Here is one that makes use of the properties of both a rectangle and a rhombus: Construct a segment and its midpoint. Mark the midpoint as a center. Select the segment and its endpoints and rotate the segment by 90°. You have just created the diagonals of a square. Connect the endpoints to create the square.

4. If students have a parallelogram tool, they can save time by using it here.

a. The angle bisectors of opposite angles of a parallelogram are parallel. Here is one explanation of why this is true. Since opposite angles of a parallelogram are congruent, $m\angle BAG = m\angle CDF$. Therefore, the two angle bisectors create four smaller congruent angles. One pair of these is $\angle FAC$ and $\angle CDG$. Since opposite sides of a parallelogram are parallel, we know that $m\angle FAC = m\angle HFD$ because these are corresponding angles. Therefore, $m\angle CDG = m\angle HFD$. Since these are corresponding angles of the two angle bisectors with segment *BD* as the transversal, we can conclude that the angle bisectors are parallel.

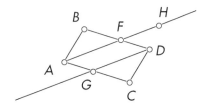

b. Angle bisectors of adjacent angles of a parallelogram are perpendicular.

Adjacent angles in a parallelogram are supplementary, and the angle bisectors split these adjacent angles in half. So $\angle ABE$ and $\angle EAB$ are complementary. The remaining angle in triangle *AEB* must measure 90°, since the first 90° has already been used up by the complementary angles. Therefore, the angle bisectors are perpendicular.

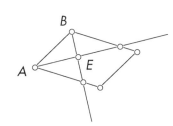

Lesson 7.1

Defining Circles

Example Sketches

- Circles 1 (Mac) or ch07\circles1.gsp (Windows)
- Circles 2 (Mac) or ch07\circles2.gsp (Windows)
- Circles 3 (Mac) or ch07\circles3.gsp (Windows)
- Circles 4 (Mac) or ch07\circles4.gsp (Windows)

Discovering Geometry Correlation/Lesson Guide

This activity replaces Lesson 7.1 in *Discovering Geometry*. In addition to arriving at definitions of parts of circles, students get experience with circles in a dynamic geometry environment. Since the text lesson has no hands-on investigations, this lesson is a good candidate for a trip to the computer lab.

Construction Tips: Defining Circle Terms

Step 1: Naming circles after two points is unconventional, but it's convenient when referring to Sketchpad circles. See the answer to question 3 below.

Investigate

1. *AC* doesn't change. A circle is defined as the set of all points in a plane at a given distance from a given point in the plane. Point *C* can represent any point on the circle, and *AC* is the given distance from the given point, point *A*.

2. The three commands in the Measure menu that can be used to measure the radius of a circle are Radius (select the circle), Distance (select the center and a point on the circle), and Length (select a segment drawn from the center to a point on the circle).

3. Infinitely many circles can share the same center. Naming a circle after two points can prevent confusion when more than one circle share the same center. Since Sketchpad circles come with two points—one defining the center and the other defining the radius—it's particularly convenient to name Sketchpad circles after two points.

4. Congruent circles are circles that have the same radius. Note: The Construct menu command Circle By Center+Radius is very useful in many constructions. It gives you a fixed radius compass (unlike the freehand Circle tool) for duplicating lengths.

Construction Tips: Defining Arcs

Steps 3 and 4: The order in which you select points is important in these steps! Selecting point *B* and then point *C* in step 3 gives a different arc than selecting point *C* and then point *B* in step 4. Sketchpad constructs an arc defined by two points selected in counterclockwise order. Therefore, one selection order gives the minor arc and the other selection order gives the major arc. It's convenient to be able to do this in a dynamic geometry environment in which an arc can't be expected to stay one type or another all the time. But defining major arcs by two points is contrary to arc naming conventions in most textbooks, including *Discovering Geometry,* in which an arc named after two points is assumed to be a minor arc. In books, an arc *BC* would be the same as an arc *CB*. Explain this to students if confusion arises.

Investigate

5. The major arc can be named $\overset{\frown}{BDC}$ or $\overset{\frown}{CDB}$.

6. Because two points can divide a circle into two semicircles, it's necessary to distinguish one semicircle from the other by naming them after three points. Students should add a point *E* to their sketches. One semicircle is named $\overset{\frown}{BDC}$ or $\overset{\frown}{CDB}$, and the other semicircle is named $\overset{\frown}{BEC}$ or $\overset{\frown}{CEB}$.

7. A chord is a segment whose endpoints are points on a circle.

8. A diameter is a chord that passes through the center of the circle.

9. A secant is a line that intersects a circle at two points.

10. A tangent is a line that intersects a circle at exactly one point.

11. An inscribed angle is an angle whose vertex is on a circle and whose sides intersect the circle.

12. Infinitely many angles intersect a given arc. Because point C is dynamic, $\angle BCD$ represents all the inscribed angles that intercept $\overarc{BD}$.

13. When point C passes point D or point B to lie on $\overarc{BD}$, it no longer intercepts $\overarc{BD}$. Instead, it intercepts the major arc opposite $\overarc{BD}$.

14. A central angle is an angle whose vertex is at the center of a circle.

Explore More

1. Method 1: Construct a circle AB. Mark point A as a center for rotation and rotate point B by 180°. Construct diameter BB'. This method is nice because both points B and B' are fully draggable.

   Method 2: Construct a circle AB and a line AB. Construct point C where the line intersects the circle. Construct diameter CB.

   It may be easiest to construct a circle given a diameter (though that wasn't the task): Construct a segment and its midpoint. Construct a circle from this midpoint to either endpoint.

2. Construct a circle and a radius segment. Through the radius endpoint on the circle, construct a line perpendicular to the radius.

Lesson 7.2

Discovering Chord Properties

Example Sketches

• Chords 1 (Mac) or ch07\chords1.gsp (Windows)

• Chords 2 (Mac) or ch07\chords2.gsp (Windows)

Discovering Geometry Correlation/Lesson Guide

This activity replaces Lesson 7.2 in *Discovering Geometry*. One slight difference is that here students arrive at C-64 out of order, in Investigation 7.2.1 instead of in Investigation 7.2.2 as in the text.

Construction Tips: Investigation 7.2.1

Step 5: Students can look at the prompter in the bottom left corner of the sketch to confirm that they're releasing the mouse button at an intersection.

Step 6: Be sure students don't hide the wrong circle. The circle to be hidden is shown dashed in the figure.

Investigate

1. If two chords in a circle are congruent, then they determine two central angles that are congruent (C-61).

2. If two chords in a circle are congruent, then their intercepted arcs are congruent (C-62). Note: This conjecture follows directly from C-61.

3. Two congruent chords in a circle are equally distant from the center of the circle (C-64). Note: This conjecture is not misnumbered. Here it comes in a different order from the order in *Discovering Geometry*.

4. The perpendicular intersects the chord at the chord's midpoint. The perpendicular from the center of a circle to a chord is the perpendicular bisector of the chord (C-63).

5. The perpendicular bisector of a chord passes through the center of the circle (C-65).

6. Construct two chords and their perpendicular bisectors. The circle's center is the point where these perpendicular bisectors intersect.

Explore More

1. Because all radii of a circle are congruent, two congruent chords define two congruent triangles by SSS. Thus, the central angles they define are congruent by CPCTC.

2. A longer chord in a circle is closer to the center of the circle. The longest possible chords in a circle are diameters.

3. If two congruent segments are chords of noncongruent circles, the chord in the larger circle will define a smaller central angle. You can return to this question after students have studied trigonometry and show that the measure of a central angle is equal to $2\tan^{-1}(l/2r)$ where l is the length of the chord and r is the radius of the circle. As r increases, the value of this expression decreases.

Lesson 7.3

Discovering Tangent Properties

Example Sketches

- Tangents 1 (Mac) or ch07\tangents1.gsp (Windows)
- Tangents 2 (Mac) or ch07\tangents2.gsp (Windows)

Discovering Geometry Correlation/Lesson Guide

This activity replaces Lesson 7.3 in *Discovering Geometry*, but students should look in the text at the examples of externally and internally tangent circles and the example of tangential velocity. Most important, they shouldn't miss the poem that opens the lesson in the text!

Construction Tips: Investigation 7.3.1

Step 4: Make sure students measure the correct angle. They need to measure the angle whose vertex is the radius endpoint.

Investigate

1. Depending on the precision with which students are displaying angle measures, the measure of ∠CBA should be very close to 90°. A tangent to a circle is perpendicular to the radius drawn to the point of tangency (C-66: Tangent Conjecture).

Construction Tips: Investigation 7.3.2

Step 5: Use the method described in step 3.

Step 6: Students may need to do some dragging to bring this intersection onto their screens.

Investigate

2. Tangent segments to a circle from a point outside the circle are congruent (C-67: Tangent Segments Conjecture).

Explore More

To construct two tangents to circle *AB* from point *C* outside the circle, construct $\overline{CA}$ and its midpoint *D*. Construct circle *DA* and points *E* and *F* where circle *DA* intersects circle *AB*. Points *E* and *F* are points of tangency for lines drawn from point *C*. This works because angles *AEC* and *AFC* are inscribed in semicircles and are thus right angles.

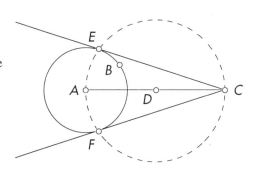

Lesson 7.4

Arcs and Angles

Example Sketches

- Arcs & Angles 1 (Mac) or ch07\arcang1.gsp (Windows)
- Arcs & Angles 2 (Mac) or ch07\arcang2.gsp (Windows)
- Arcs & Angles 3 (Mac) or ch07\arcang3.gsp (Windows)

Discovering Geometry Correlation/Lesson Guide

This activity replaces Lesson 7.4 in *Discovering Geometry*.

Construction Tips: Investigations 7.4.1–7.4.3

Step 5: Selection order is important here. Sketchpad constructs arcs defined by two points in counterclockwise order around the circle. Arcs so defined are not necessarily minor arcs!

Step 6: You can tell whether a click selects the arc or the circle by where the selection indicators appear. If clicking selects the circle, just click again to select the arc that overlaps the circle.

Investigate

1. The measure of an inscribed angle in a circle is half the measure of the arc it intercepts (C-68: Inscribed Angle Conjecture).

2. The computer isn't broken. Dragging point C doesn't change the arc; thus, it doesn't change the measure of the inscribed angle that intercepts it. Students often don't think of a single dynamic angle as representing many angles. (Instead, they think of it as a single angle that moves.) So they may need to construct a second angle to be convinced of this conjecture: Inscribed angles that intercept the same arc are congruent (C-69).

3. The measure of $\angle DCB$ should be close to 90°. Angles inscribed in a semicircle are right angles (C-70).

Construction Tips: Investigation 7.4.4

Step 4: Students should double-check that they've measured the four different angles in the quadrilateral. No two of the four angle measurements should have the same middle letter. If they do, students are apt to jump to an incorrect conclusion that pairs of angles are equal in measure.

Investigate

4. The opposite angles of a quadrilateral inscribed in a circle are supplementary (C-71).

5. The two arcs intercepted by opposite angles in the quadrilateral comprise the entire circle. Hence, the sum of their measures is 360°. Therefore, the sum of the angles that intercept them is (1/2)360° = 180°.

Construction Tips: Investigation 7.4.5

Steps 6 and 7: Again, when constructing arcs defined by two points, selection order is important. If students get the wrong arc, they should undo their selection and try again, being careful about selection order.

Investigate

6. Parallel lines intercept congruent arcs on a circle (C-72).

Lesson 7.5

The Circumference/Diameter Ratio

Example Sketches

• Circumference/Diameter (Mac) or ch07\circdiam.gsp (Windows)

Discovering Geometry Correlation/Lesson Guide

Use this activity in place of, or as an extension to, Lesson 7.5 in *Discovering Geometry*. The hands-on investigation as described in the text is fun, so you might choose to do this activity as a follow-up demonstration on a single computer with an overhead display.

Construction Tips

Step 6: Selection order is important because when students later graph the data in this table they'll want the diameter values on the *x*-axis.

Investigate

1. The plotted points should be collinear.

2. The ray actually passes through all the points on the graph. The slope of the ray is about 3.14. Since the ray starts at the origin, its rise/run is just y/x, or circumference/diameter. Thus, the slope represents the ratio of the circle's circumference to its diameter.

3. The plotted point moves along the ray, so the ray represents all ordered pairs (D, C), where D is the diameter and C is the circumference of any circle. For all circles, C/D is a constant (the slope of the ray).

4. If C is the circumference and D is the diameter of a circle, then there is a number π such that $C = \pi D$. Because $D = 2r$, where r is the radius, then $C = 2\pi r$ (C-73: Circumference Conjecture).

Lesson 8.1

Transformations

Example Sketches

• Transformations (Mac) or ch08\transfrm.gsp (Windows)

Discovering Geometry Correlation/Lesson Guide

This activity replaces Lesson 8.1 from *Discovering Geometry*. Explore More 1 and 2 introduce transformation notation for the *x-y* coordinate system. These problems are challenging and will help students with Exercises 18–21. Explore More 3 introduces glide reflections as well as custom transformations, a neat feature of Sketchpad. You can do Explore More 3 without first doing Explore More 1 and 2.

Construction Tips

Step 1: It's worth following the shortcut for constructing the letter.

Step 2: If it is necessary to change the labels to *K* and *L*, double-click the labels with the Text tool.

Step 4: To change shading or color, use the Display menu.

Step 5: It might help to label the original letter *F Original*. It is also fun to drag the vertices of the original *F* and observe how this affects the image shape.

Step 6: Make sure the segments are attached correctly at point *N*. Also, it might help students to relabel point *N* as *Center*.

Step 11: You might have students drag *N*, the center of rotation, as well.

Investigate

1. The only images that can lie directly on top of each other are the rotated and translated images. This happens only when the vector *KL* has a length of zero and the angle *MNO* has a measure of zero. In this case, both images lie on top of the original.

2. a. A translated image has a different location from the original (unless the translation vector has length zero).

   b. A translated image is congruent to the original and has the same orientation.

3. a. A rotated image has a different location from the original and is also turned at a different angle. (Again, neither statement is true if the angle of rotation is zero.)

   b. A rotated image is congruent to the original and is *not* a mirror image.

4. a. A reflected image has a reverse orientation from the original. It looks like a mirror image.

   b. A reflected image is congruent to the original.

Explore More

1. Make sure students scale their axes, especially if the units of the grid are in inches. Also make sure they have Snap To Grid checked in the Graph menu, although this will be checked automatically as the default setting.

   This transformation is a translation by a vector that points horizontally to the left three units. (Point *L* is three units to the left of point *K*.)

2. This transformation is a reflection across the *y*-axis.

3. Step 1: To create a glide reflection, translate the object by any vector; then reflect the object across any mirror line. It actually does not matter whether you translate or reflect first (you might ask students to investigate this). It's also not necessary for the vector to be parallel to the mirror line, although if it's not the mirror line will not be the line of glide reflection symmetry.

   a. A translation is like a glide, and you also use a reflection. Thus, this transformation is called a glide reflection.

   b. Each successive footstep has the opposite orientation, since it is the imprint of the opposite foot. This causes the reflection. The person's moving along down the beach causes the translation, or glide.

Lesson 8.2

Properties of Isometries

Example Sketches

- Isometries (Mac) or ch08\isometr.gsp

Discovering Geometry Correlation/Lesson Guide

This activity replaces Lesson 8.2 from *Discovering Geometry*. The investigations are in a different order here (8.2.3 comes before 8.2.2). This rearrangement makes sense because on the computer it is easy to treat the case of reflections across two parallel lines as a special case of reflections across any two lines.

Construction Tips: Investigation 8.2.1

Step 5: Make sure students click the actual measurements to insert them in the calculator and don't just type in values.

Step 7: To reflect point D, select it and choose Reflect in the Transform menu.

Investigate

1. Students should place point E so that the incoming and outgoing angle measures are equal. It might be hard to get the angles exactly equal, especially if the measurements are very precise. To change precision, use the Preferences sub-menu in the Display menu.

2. Drag point E so it lies on segment CD'. This gives the minimal path for the cue ball, which is also the path of a reflection. The path is minimal because it is the same length as $\overline{CD}$. CD is the shortest distance from C to D, and therefore a corresponding reflected path of the same length is the shortest path from C, to the segment to D.

3. $CE + ED$ is at a minimum when point E is at the correct location. This is because the correct path is also the shortest path.

4. If points A and B are on one side of line l, then the minimal path from point A to line l to point B is found by reflecting point B over line l, drawing segment AB', then drawing segments AC and CB, where point C is the point of intersection of segment AB' and line l (C-75: Minimal Path Conjecture).

Construction Tips: Investigation 8.2.3

Steps 1–4: The point labels help distinguish between the original figure, the first reflected image, and the second reflected image.

Investigate

5. The rotated image can coincide with the second reflected image, so a double reflection across two intersecting lines is equivalent to a single rotation.

6. When the transformed images coincide, the smaller angle between the mirror lines is exactly half the angle of rotation of the rotated image.

7. A reflection over a line followed by a reflection of the image over a second line that intersects the first line is equivalent to a single rotation. The measure of the angle of rotation is equal to twice the measure of the angle between the pair of intersecting reflection lines (C-77).

Construction Tips: Investigation 8.2.2

Step 5: Make sure every angle measurement disappears. The rotated image should also disappear at this point.

Investigate

8. The distance between the original figure and its image is twice the distance between the parallel lines.

9. If you translated the original polygon by twice the distance between the parallel lines, you would get the second image.

10. A reflection over a line followed by a reflection of the image over a second line parallel to the first is equivalent to a single translation. In addition, the distance from any point to its second image under the two reflections is twice the distance between the parallel lines (C-76).

Explore More

1. After hiding the center of rotation, students should redo the construction from Investigation 8.2.3. After dragging the lines and changing the angles until the rotated and double reflected images coincide, they should choose Show All Hidden in the Display menu. They will notice that the center of rotation coincides with the intersection point of the mirror lines.

2. A triple reflection is equivalent to a glide reflection. Note that once you have created a custom transformation it appears as the last item in the Transform menu. To use it, you can either choose it from the menu or use the keyboard shortcut indicated near its name on the menu.

Lesson 8.3

Symmetry

Example Sketches

Symmetry (Mac) or ch08\symmetry.gsp (Windows)

Discovering Geometry Correlation/Lesson Guide

This activity replaces Investigation 8.3 in Lesson 8.3 from *Discovering Geometry*. There's a lot of introductory material on pages 386 and 387 in *Discovering Geometry* that students should read and/or discuss in class.

Construction Tips

Step 1: This exploration can go fairly quickly if students use script tools. Sample scripts for many regular polygons can be found in the Regular Polygons folder (Mac) or Regpoly directory (Windows) on the disk that comes with this book. Some of these polygons already have centers. To set a Script tool folder, choose Preferences in the Display menu and click More. In the Advanced Preferences dialog, under Set Script Tool Folder, click Set. (You may first have to click Clear.) Navigate in the pop-up menu to find the desired folder. Click the Set button. Click Continue, and then click OK to dismiss the Preferences dialog.

Step 2: This step is necessary only if the center isn't a script given. See what methods students come up with for constructing centers. In even-sided polygons, they can construct two segments connecting pairs of opposite vertices. In odd-sided polygons, they'll need to connect vertices with midpoints of opposite sides.

Step 3: Make sure students don't use any points on their figures to construct the line. The line should be free to move independently of the figure.

Investigate

1. Students should discover lines of symmetry by positioning the line so that the image lands perfectly on top of the original. For the equilateral triangle shown here, a line of symmetry passes through a vertex and the midpoint of the opposite side. A line of symmetry in an even-sided regular polygon passes through either a pair of opposite vertices or a pair of opposite midpoints.

2. See the table for question 5 below for totals in various polygons.

3. In the case of the equilateral triangle, students will find that the image coincides with the original when the angle is opened to 120°. In a regular n-gon, a rotation of $360°/n$ will cause the image to coincide with the original.

4. In the case of the equilateral triangle, students will find that the image coincides with the original three times as they change the angle through one complete revolution. Unless they've chosen directed degrees for angle measure under Preferences, however, two of the angles will measure 120°. (Directed degrees will display the angles as 120° and −120°.) You may also have to point out that students should count the 360° rotation.

5.

Number of sides of regular polygon	3	4	5	6	...	8	...	n
Number of reflectional symmetries	3	4	5	6	...	8	...	n
Number of rotational symmetries	3	4	5	6	...	8	...	n

6. A regular polygon of n sides has n reflectional symmetries and n rotational symmetries. The measure of the smallest angle of rotation for a rotational symmetry of a regular polygon of n sides is $360°/n$ (C-78).

Explore More

1. Using rotations is the easiest way to construct a regular polygon. Rotate a point around another point $n − 1$ times by an angle of $360°/n$ to construct the n vertices of the polygon. Students can also use rotations to construct part of a polygon and then finish it off using reflections.

2. Rhombuses and rectangles have two lines of symmetry and 180° rotational symmetry. Isosceles trapezoids and kites have one line of symmetry.

Lesson 8.6

Tessellations Using Only Translations

Example Sketches

• Translation tessellation (Mac) or ch08\transtes.gsp (Windows)

Discovering Geometry Correlation/Lesson Guide

This activity explains how to make a tessellation using translations. It starts with a parallelogram. In Explore More 2, students make a translational tessellation starting with a regular hexagon. The directions in Lesson 8.6 in *Discovering Geometry* start with a square, so this activity is slightly more challenging and certainly covers the same material.

It's fun for students to print these out, but printing depends on the availability of a printer. You probably don't have a color printer, so remind students that color will not show up. Also, the darker shades waste a lot of toner. It might be best for students to print out only the edges of the tiles and then color in the tiles by hand. It's a good idea to have students choose Print Preview before they print and scale their drawing to fit on a single page. This will save paper.

Construction Tips

This sketch contains lots of steps. If students work carefully, they shouldn't have much trouble, and they will find the end result worthwhile. When students mark vectors, they should watch the screen carefully to see it indicate the vector marked. This helps make it clear to them what they did during that step.

Explore More

1. This is an easy extension, and it can have dramatic results. It might be more convenient to make an animation button so you can turn the animation on and off. To do this, select the same circle and point, but go to the Edit menu, choose Action Button, and then choose Animation. The animation is likely to cause edges of the tile to intersect. If so, students should adjust the circle so this doesn't happen.

2. If students have trouble with this construction, they can follow the steps outlined at the bottom of page 409 in *Discovering Geometry*.

Lesson 8.7

Tessellations That Use Rotations

Example Sketches

• Rotation Tessellation (Mac) or ch08\rottess.gsp (Windows)

Discovering Geometry Correlation/Lesson Guide

This activity explains how to make a tessellation using rotations. It starts with an equilateral triangle. In Explore More 1, students follow the directions from *Discovering Geometry* to make a rotational tessellation starting with a regular hexagon, and in Explore More 2 they do the same with a parallelogram. The directions in Lesson 8.7 in *Discovering Geometry* start with a regular hexagon and then show an equilateral triangle, so the activity here covers pretty much the same material as the student text.

It's fun for students to print these out, but printing depends on the availability of a printer. You probably don't have a color printer, so remind students that color will not show up. Also, the darker shades waste a lot of toner. It might be best for students to print out only the edges of the tiles and then color in the tiles by hand. It's a good idea to have students choose Print Preview before they print and scale their drawing to fit on a single page. This will save paper.

Construction Tips

Step 10: This is a difficult process that requires careful visualizing and patience. Remind students that positive angles rotate the figure counterclockwise. Since students used point *A* as a center of 60° rotations in the construction of the tile, it works as a center for 60° rotations here. Likewise, they should use point *F* as a center for a 180° rotation. Unless students rotated some points as well as the polygon interiors, they will eventually run out of centers of rotation to continue the tiling process. If they still wish to continue, have them rotate a few points strategically to form new rotation centers for the outer regions of the tiling.

Explore More

These tessellations are actually slightly simpler than the one described in this activity. Encourage students to try these, but give them enough time to complete them.

Lesson 9.1

Areas of Rectangles and Parallelograms

Example Sketches

• Parallelogram Area (Mac) or ch09\pararea.gsp (Windows)

Discovering Geometry Correlation/Lesson Guide

Use this lesson in place of, or as an extension to, Lesson 9.1 in *Discovering Geometry*. In this lesson, students construct a rectangle and write a formula for its area in terms of its base b and height h. Then students construct a parallelogram that has the same base and height as the rectangle. By changing the shape of the parallelogram without changing its base or its height, students will observe that its area is the same as the area of the rectangle.

Construction Tips: Investigation 9.1.1

Step 1: Holding down the Shift key while drawing a segment makes it easy to draw a horizontal segment.

Step 2: Select both points and the segment. Choose Perpendicular Line in the Construct menu to get both lines.

Step 7: To show a segment's label, click once on the segment with the Text tool. To change the label, double-click on the label with the Text tool.

Investigate

1. The area of a rectangle is given by the formula $A = bh$, where A is the area, b is the length of the base, and h is the height of the rectangle (C-81: Rectangle Area Conjecture).

Construction Tips: Investigation 9.1.2

Step 15: Select the vertices in order; then choose Polygon Interior in the Construct menu.

Investigate

2. Side lengths AG and BH change.

3. The measures b and h don't change.

4. Yes; the height of the rectangle is the same as the height of the parallelogram.

5. Yes; when point G coincides with point C, the parallelogram fills the rectangle.

6. The area of the parallelogram doesn't change when you drag point G.

7. The area of a parallelogram is given by the formula $A = bh$, where A is the area, b is the length of the base, and h is the height of the parallelogram (C-82: Parallelogram Area Conjecture).

Explore More

If you draw an altitude from the vertex of the parallelogram to the opposite side, you can cut along this altitude to cut off a triangle. That triangle will then fit the other side of the parallelogram to form a rectangle with the same base and height.

Lesson 9.2

Areas of Triangles, Trapezoids, and Kites

Example Sketches

• Triangle Area (Mac) or ch09\triarea.gsp (Windows)

Discovering Geometry Correlation/Lesson Guide

Use this activity in place of, or as an extension to, Lesson 9.2 in *Discovering Geometry*. In Investigations 9.2.1 and 9.2.2 students discover that any triangle or trapezoid can be doubled to form a parallelogram. By halving the area of the parallelogram, they arrive at formulas for the areas of a triangle and a trapezoid. Students derive the formula for the area of a kite by using the fact that the diagonals are perpendicular and one bisects the other.

The only purpose of the grid in this activity is to give students more visual feedback for their conjectures about areas.

Construction Tips: Investigation 9.2.1

Step 1: By default, Snap To Grid should be checked in the Graph menu.

Step 6: Students could simply select the entire triangle and rotate it, but then they'd get double points at point *D* and point *E,* which could cause confusion if they're showing labels.

Investigate

1. The figure is a parallelogram.

2. $A = bh$

3. The area of the triangle is half the area of the parallelogram.

4. The area of a triangle is given by the formula $A = (1/2)bh,$ where A is the area, b is the length of the base, and h is the height of the triangle (C-83: Triangle Area Conjecture).

Construction Tips: Investigation 9.2.2

Step 7: Click once on a segment to show its label. Double-click on the label to change it. Click Use Subscript in the Relabel dialog to make the label b_1. Otherwise, be content with the label *b1*.

Investigate

5. The quadrilateral is a parallelogram.

6. $b_1 + b_2$

7. The area of a trapezoid is given by the formula $A = (1/2)(b_1 + b_2)h,$ where A is the area, b_1 and b_2 are the lengths of the two bases, and h is the height of the trapezoid (C-84: Trapezoid Area Conjecture).

Construction Tips: Investigation 9.2.3

This construction gives a kite that can be manipulated into a dart (a concave kite). However, the formula that students derive for area will still work.

Investigate

8. Answers will vary. The area of a kite is given by the formula $A = (1/2)d_1d_2,$ where A is the area, and d_1 and d_2 are the lengths of the two diagonals (C-85: Kite Area Conjecture).

Explore More

1. In Lesson 9.1 of this book, students construct a parallelogram whose perimeter can be changed without changing the area. They can do similar constructions for triangles and trapezoids.

2. Answers will vary. One possible answer: The area of quadrilateral *ABCD* is given by the formula $A = (1/2)dh_1 + (1/2)dh_2$, where d is the length of diagonal *AC* and h_1 and h_2 are the lengths of the altitudes drawn to that diagonal from points *B* and *D*.

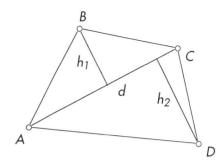

Lesson 9.4

Areas of Regular Polygons

Required Sketches

- 5/Pentagon (By Edge) (Mac) or regpoly\4byeedge.gss (Windows)

Discovering Geometry Correlation/Lesson Guide

Use this lesson in place of, or as an extension to, Lesson 9.4 in *Discovering Geometry*. Students will use script tools to construct regular polygons.

Construction Tips

Step 1: If you have the folders that came with Sketchpad accessible, you can have students select the folder containing sample scripts to set their Script tool folder.

Step 2: Script tools for inscribed polygons create center points.

Step 3: The polygon interiors just get in the way. To delete an interior, click anywhere on it to select it; then press the Delete key on the keyboard.

Step 4: To construct the center of an even-sided polygon, construct two diagonals and their point of intersection. For an odd-sided polygon, construct midpoints of two sides and connect them with segments to opposite vertices. The center is at the intersection of these segments.

Investigate/Conjecture

1. Five triangles were formed.

2. The triangles are congruent. Explanations will vary. Students can write an argument that shows the triangles are congruent using SSS, SAS, ASA, or AAS.

3. $A = (1/2)bh$

4. $A = (1/2)sa$

5. $A = (5)(1/2)sa$

6. n triangles

7. The area of a regular polygon is given by the formula $A = (1/2)asn$, where A is the area, a is the apothem, s is the length of each side, and n is the number of sides of the regular polygon.

8. Because the length of each side times the number of sides is the perimeter, $sn = p$. The formula can also be written as $A = (1/2)ap$ (C-86: Regular Polygon Area Conjecture).

Explore More

See student sketches.

Lesson 9.5

Areas of Circles

Required Sketch

• To a Circle (Mac) or ch09\polycirc.gsp (Windows)

Discovering Geometry Correlation/Lesson Guide

Use this lesson in place of, or as an extension to, Lesson 9.5 in *Discovering Geometry*. This activity uses a different approach: Instead of cutting up sectors and arranging them into a shape that resembles a parallelogram, students derive the formula for the area of a circle from the regular polygon area formula. You might choose to have students do the investigation in the text; then you can demonstrate this activity using a computer with an overhead display device.

Investigate

1. The polygon begins to fill the circle. Its area approaches that of the circle as the number of sides increases.

2. $C = 2\pi r$

3. $A = (1/2)ap$

4. $A = (1/2)rC$

5. $A = (1/2)rC = (1/2)r(2\pi r) = \pi r^2$

Lesson 10.1

The Theorem of Pythagoras

Example Sketches

• Pythagorean Theorem (Mac) or ch10\pythag.gsp (Windows)

Discovering Geometry Correlation/Lesson Guide

This activity replaces Lesson 10.1 in *Discovering Geometry*. One difference in the investigation here is that students arrive at the theorem before they do the dissection. Be sure to save time at the end of class to go over a couple of examples of how to use the theorem, or at least direct students' attention to the examples in the text so that students can do the homework.

Construction Tips

Step 3: Make sure students use point B for the radius point and that they don't just draw a circle that happens to pass through point B.

Step 7: If students have trouble with squares that go the wrong way, have them undo and try again with a different selection order.

Investigate

1. The sum of the areas of the squares on the leg is equal to the area of the square on the hypotenuse.

2. a^2

3. In a right triangle, if a and b are the lengths of the legs and c is the length of the hypotenuse, then $a^2 + b^2 = c^2$.

Construction Tips

Step 9: To delete the interior, click on it to select it, then press the Delete key on the keyboard.

Investigate

4. See the solution at right. Note: Once the pieces are cut, they are no longer related to the squares from which they came. Thus if you change the triangle, the pieces won't fit anymore. If you want to try the experiment for a different triangle, undo until the pieces are back in their original places, then change the triangle and repeat the experiment.

5. Because the pieces from the squares on the legs of the right triangle fit perfectly into the square on the hypotenuse, they must occupy the same area. Therefore, the sum of the areas of the squares on the legs of the right triangle is equal to the area of the square on the hypotenuse.

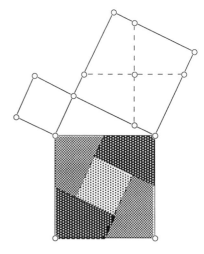

Lesson 10.2

Is the Converse True?

Required Sketch

• Triple Checker (Mac) or ch10\triplchk.gsp (Windows)

Example Sketch

• Pythagorean Converse (Mac) or ch10\pythconv.gsp (Windows)

Discovering Geometry Correlation/Lesson Guide

This activity replaces Lesson 10.2 in *Discovering Geometry*. The approach in the text is different: students try Pythagorean triples to see if they work in the formula. In this activity students start with an arbitrary triangle with squares on the sides and see that when the sum of the areas of the squares on the legs is equal to the area of the square on the hypotenuse, the triangle is a right triangle. Pythgagorean triples are introduced as a follow-up to the main investigation.

In the second Investigate question, students open a pre-made sketch and investigate triples. The sketch they use for this activity is the same one they use in Lesson 10.5: Multiples of Right Triangles. You can probably combine Lesson 10.5 with this one.

Construction Tips

Step 2: This step assumes students are familiar with using scripts as script tools. Set a script tool folder that has a script for a square in it. To set a script tool folder, choose Preferences in the Display menu and click More. In the Advanced Preferences dialog, under Set Script Tool Folder, click Set. (You may first have to click Clear.) Navigate in the pop-up menu to find the desired folder. Click the Set button. Click Continue, then click OK to dismiss the Preferences dialog.

Step 3: Hold down the Shift key and click on all three interiors to select them. Choose Area in the Measure menu.

Step 4: Double-click on a measure to get the calculator. Click on a measure in the sketch to enter it into the calculator.

Investigate

1. Students should get a right triangle. If angle measures are off a bit, point out that students may not have been able to make the area sum exactly equal to the area of the third square. Students should conjecture: If the lengths of the three sides of a triangle work in the Pythagorean formula, then the triangle is a right triangle (C-89: Converse of the Pythagorean Theorem).

2. Choice e, 9-12-17, is not a Pythagorean triple: $9^2 + 12^2 < 17^2$. In fact, students may discover that $9^2 + 12^2 = 15^2$.

Lesson 10.4

Two Special Right Triangles

Example Sketches

• Special Right Δ's (Mac) or ch10\sprttri.gsp (Windows)

Discovering Geometry Correlation/Lesson Guide

Use this activity in place of, or as an extension to, Lesson 10.4 in *Discovering Geometry*. In Investigation 10.4.1 in the text, students practice simplifying radicals. This practice is necessary for the repeated-calculations approach used in Investigation 10.4.2, but it's not necessary for the approach in this activity. In this activity, students arrive at the conjectures by investigating relationships among the actual squares instead of by discovering patterns in the calculations. Students will probably need some guidance on the last question of each investigation. You might want to go over questions 3 and 8 with the whole class.

Construction Tips: Investigation 10.4.2

Step 1: This step assumes students are familiar with using scripts as script tools. Set a script tool folder that has a script for a square in it. To set a script tool folder, choose Preferences in the Display menu and click More. In the Advanced Preferences dialog, under Set Script Tool Folder, click Set. (You may first have to click Clear.) Navigate in the pop-up menu to find the desired folder. Click the Set button. Click Continue, then click OK to dismiss the Preferences dialog.

Investigate

1. Because the acute angles in the isosceles right triangle are congruent and have measures that sum to 90°, each must measure 45°.

2. The diagonals divide each smaller square into two right triangles, each of which is congruent to the original triangle. Four of these right triangles would fit into the larger square, so if the smaller squares have area x^2, the larger square has area $2x^2$.

3. In an isosceles right triangle, if the legs have length x, then the hypotenuse has length $x\sqrt{2}$ (C-90: Isosceles Right Triangle Conjecture).

Construction Tips: Investigation 10.4.3

Step 1: A script tool for an equilateral triangle can be found in the Regular Polygons folder.

Investigate

4. Since $\triangle ABC$ is equilateral, each of its angles measures 60°. Median CD divides $\triangle ABC$ into two congruent triangles, so in $\triangle BCD$, $m\angle B = 60°$, $m\angle BCD = 30°$, and $m\angle CDB = 90°$.

5. Because point D is a midpoint, $BC = 2BD$. In a 30-60 right triangle, if the side opposite the 30° angle has length x, then the hypotenuse has length $2x$ (C-91).

6. $(2x)^2 = 4x^2$

7. $4x^2 - x^2 = 3x^2$

8. In a 30-60 right triangle, if the shorter leg has length x, then the longer leg has length $x\sqrt{3}$ and the hypotenuse has length $2x$ (C-92: 30-60 Right Triangle Conjecture).

Lesson 10.5

Multiples of Right Triangles

Required Sketch

• Triple Check (Mac) or ch10\triplchk.gsp (Windows)

Discovering Geometry Correlation/Lesson Guide

This activity replaces Lesson 10.5 in *Discovering Geometry*. The sketch students use for this activity is the same one they use in Lesson 10.2: Is the converse true? If you do that activity, you might want to combine this investigation with it. This activity does not cover conjecture C-94.

Construction Tips

Step 2: Make sure students do this. If they don't, the investigation in question 3 won't work.

Investigate

1. When $a = 4$ and $b = 5$, $c \approx 6.403$, which is not an integer.

2. Adding the same amount to each leg length in a Pythagorean triple does not yield another triple; the hypotenuse length is not an integer.

3. If the triangle doesn't stay a right triangle, students failed to mark point C as the center for dilation. Students will need to watch carefully as they drag in order to record all triples that are multiples of the one they started with. They should record at least the triples 6-8-10, 9-12-15, and 12-16-20.

4. Students should get a 10-24-26 right triangle. They should guess that the next triple would be 15-36-39, or 3(5)-3(12)-3(13).

5. $16^2 + 30^2 = 256 + 900 = 1156 = 34^2$

6. 7-24-25

7. If you multiply the lengths of all three sides of any right triangle by the same number, the resulting triangle will be a right triangle (C-93: Pythagorean Multiples Conjecture).

Discovering Geometry with The Geometer's Sketchpad **179**

Lesson 10.7
Distance in Coordinate Geometry

Required Sketch

• Coordinate Distance (Mac) or ch10\distance.gsp (Windows)

Discovering Geometry Correlation/Lesson Guide

This activity replaces Lesson 10.9 in *Discovering Geometry*. It uses a pre-made sketch, and most of the investigating is done with the calculator and with paper and pencil.

Investigate

1. $x_D - x_C$

2. $y_D - y_C$

3. $CE^2 + DE^2 = CD^2$

4. $\sqrt{(x_D - x_C)^2 + (y_D - y_C)^2}$

5. $AB^2 = (x_2 - x_1)^2 + (y_2 - y_1)^2$; $AB = \sqrt{(x_2 - x_1)^2 + (y_2 - y_1)^2}$ (C-95: Distance Formula)

6. Point F traces out a circle.

7. The equation for a circle with radius r and center (h, k) is $(x - h)^2 + (y - k)^2 = r^2$ (C-96: Equation of a Circle).

Lesson 12.2

Similarity

Example Sketches

• Similarity (Mac) or ch12\similar.gsp (Windows)

Discovering Geometry Correlation/Lesson Guide

This activity replaces most of Lesson 12.2 in *Discovering Geometry*. This lesson is shorter than the one in the student text but covers the same concepts. In this lesson, students have a chance to write the definition of similarity themselves. This lesson does not explain similarity notation or how to solve for missing parts in similar polygons. You might start with Investigation 12.2.1 in the book to give students a chance to experience similarity using hand measuring tools, and then continue with this lesson on the computer.

Construction Tips

Step 3: You need to select just the segments, not the endpoints. Selecting a short and then a long segment marks a ratio less than 1, which shrinks objects. Reversing the selection order marks a ratio greater than 1, which enlarges objects.

Step 4: Choose Dilate in the Transform menu.

Investigate

1. Dragging the center will change the position of the dilated image. Changing the ratio segments will change the scale factor, making the dilated image larger or smaller. When the ratio segments are equal in length, the dilated image will coincide with the original.

2. Yes, congruent polygons are also similar. When the marked ratio is equal to 1, the dilated image coincides with the original figure and the rotated image of the dilated image is congruent to the original figure.

3. All the ratios of corresponding sides in the similar polygons are equal to the dilation ratio.

4. Corresponding angles in similar polygons are congruent.

5. Two polygons are similar polygons if and only if the corresponding angles are congruent and the corresponding sides are proportional.

6. If one polygon is the image of another polygon under a dilation, then the polygons are similar (C-101: Dilation Similarity Conjecture).

Explore More

1. a. A ray from the center of dilation through a point on the original figure passes through the corresponding point on the dilated image.

   b. The ratio of the distances from the center to a point on the original polygon and from the center to the corresponding point on the dilated image is equal to the dilation ratio, which is equal to the ratio of corresponding side lengths.

2. Answers will vary. Here's one example: In the figure at right, $\triangle ABC \sim \triangle DFE$.

3. Answers will vary. For example, a rectangle has angles congruent to the angles in a square, but the rectangle need not be similar to the square.

4. Answers will vary. For example, a rhombus may have sides that are proportional to the sides of a square, but the corresponding angles need not be congruent.

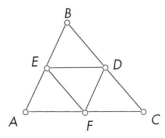

Lesson 12.3

Similar Triangles

Required Sketches

- AAA Similarity? (Mac) or ch12\AAA_sim.gsp (Windows)
- SSS Similarity? (Mac) or ch12\SSS_sim.gsp (Windows)
- SSA Similarity? (Mac) or ch12\SSA_sim.gsp (Windows)
- SAS Similarity? (Mac) or ch12\SAS_sim.gsp (Windows)

Discovering Geometry Correlation/Lesson Guide

This activity replaces Lesson 12.3 in *Discovering Geometry*. The structure of the activity is slightly different. *Discovering Geometry* addresses first the SSS Similarity Conjecture in Investigation 12.3.1, then the AA Similarity Conjecture in 12.3.2, then the SAS Similarity Conjecture as well as the lack of an SSA Similarity Conjecture in Investigation 12.3.3. This activity addresses all four possible conjectures in one investigation. As indicated in the student's version of this lesson, it makes sense to share these four different possible similarity conjectures among different groups in the class. Then you can have the different groups present and share their results.

Investigate

1. a. Any angle in the given is congruent to a pair of corresponding angles in the "triangles" above the given.

    b. Any side in the given is congruent to the corresponding side in the first "triangle" above the given and proportional to the corresponding side in the second "triangle."

    c. The ratio in the given equals the ratio between any corresponding sides of the triangles controlled by segments in the given.

2. Encourage students to change the givens as well as the movable parts of the triangles themselves. Some givens simply can't make triangles (for example, if the three sides don't obey the triangle inequality). When students can create triangles, they should observe that they are similar except in the SSA case.

3. This gives students a chance to measure to test for similarity. Again, all cases should test out to be similar except the SSA case. Students should measure any pairs of angles not controlled by the given, as well as the ratios of any sides not controlled by the given. The corresponding angles should be congruent, and the corresponding sides should be in the same ratio as the given ratio. If the points in the fractured triangles aren't exactly coincident, the measures may not work out precisely.

4. Answers will vary. Students testing the SSA case can skip this step if they found a counterexample right away. If they didn't, make sure they do before they go on to question 5.

5. Depending on which case they studied, students should report one of the observations below:

    C-102: SSS Similarity Conjecture. If the three sides of one triangle are proportional to the three sides of another triangle, then the two triangles are similar.

    C-103: AA Similarity Conjecture. If two angles of one triangle are congruent to two angles of another triangle, then the triangles are congruent. (You might need to discuss with students why two angles will suffice instead of all three being needed.)

    C-104: SAS Similarity Conjecture. If two sides of one triangle are proportional to two sides of another triangle and the included angles are congruent, then the two triangles are similar.

    Students testing the SSA case could draw a sketch like this one:

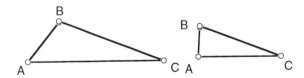

    In this case, sides *AB* and *AC* are proportional and the angles at *C* are congruent, but the triangles are not similar.

6. Students should collect all three conjectures listed above.

Explore More

1. These are good extension projects. The constructions are not easy.

   Here are steps for constructing a pair of triangles constrained by AAA: Construct the first triangle, then a line. Mark an angle in the first triangle by selecting the three points on the angle and using the Transform menu. Double-click a point on the line to mark it as a center, and rotate the line by the marked angle. Follow the same procedure on another angle and the other point on the line. The third pair of angles should take care of themselves (which is why it is really the AA Similarity Conjecture).

   The other constraints are more difficult to construct. It might be simplest to construct congruent triangles first (the construction command Circle By Center + Radius is very handy here). Then dilate sides by a marked ratio that needs to stay proportional.

2. Since both AAS and ASA require that two pairs of angles be congruent, the AA Similarity Conjecture already covers these cases. Since the triangles must already be similar by AA, the sides must be proportional. Adding the requirement that a pair of sides must be proportional wouldn't change anything, so both AAS and ASA are valid (but useless) congruence conjectures.

Lesson 12.4

Indirect Measurement with Similar Triangles

Example Sketches

• Indirect Measurement (Mac) or ch12\indirect.gsp (Windows)

Discovering Geometry Correlation/Lesson Guide

In this activity, students model a problem similar to Example A in Lesson 12.4 from *Discovering Geometry*. In Explore More, they model a problem similar to Example B. Unlike the lesson in *Discovering Geometry*, which demonstrates the solution in the sample, this activity requires students to figure out the height of the tall object on their own. For this reason, the activity here is a bit more challenging but certainly covers the same material.

If possible, find time on another day to take students outside where they can use either of these methods to find some actual heights. (See the project on page 606 in *Discovering Geometry*.)

Construction Tips

This is a good activity in which to require students to turn in a printout, if the classroom has a printer accessible. If you plan to do this, have students answer the Investigate questions on the screen with the Text tool. Also have them add color and explanations to make their sketch understandable.

Step 5: To label an object, click the object with the Text tool. To change the label, double-click the label with the Text tool and type in the new label.

Investigate

1. The triangles are similar by AAA. Since the angles of the sun's rays are essentially parallel, the angles the sun makes with the ground are congruent because they are corresponding angles (with the ground as the transversal). The angles the sun makes with the person and the tree are congruent because the sun strikes both at the same angle. The angles the person and the tree make with the ground are congruent because they both measure 90°.

2. Answers will vary depending on the sketch. If students have trouble, they can look at Example A on page 602 in *Discovering Geometry*. This example essentially gives away the process, so let them use it as a last resort. Following is a sample answer that matches the values in the picture.

   Because the triangles are similar, we can write proportion statements comparing the sides. We'll use h for the missing height of the tree.

   $$\text{You/Your shadow} = \text{Tall tree/Tree's shadow}$$

   $$0.53/0.39 = h/2.43$$

   $$h \approx 3.30$$

   This means that the tree is 330 inches tall (remember that 0.53 centimeter represented a person's height of 53 inches). This is roughly 27 feet 6 inches.

3. Answers should be close to the measured answers but might not be the same because of rounding. The variation will be even greater for actual measurements outdoors.

4. There are several ways to create similar triangles using the shadows of two objects at different times of day. Probably the most obvious way is to measure one shadow in the morning when the sun is in the east and the other in the afternoon when the sun makes the same angle from the west. Since the angle of inclination of the sun's rays is the same, the shadows create similar triangles. Students may think of other creative answers. Here are a few more:

   • If you match up the heights of the two objects and the sun's angles correctly, you can create similar triangles with one triangle sitting on its side. For example, measure a 2-foot object when it has a 1-foot shadow and then measure a 3-foot object when it has a 6-foot shadow. These triangles are similar, with sides in proportion 1 to 3.

   • Measure the objects at different times but also at different places on earth. For example, you might measure the first object at noon in Nashville, Tennessee, and the other three hours later at noon in San Francisco,

California. Since these cities are at approximately the same latitude, the angle of the sun should be the same. Some students will argue that these are not really different times of day.

• Measure the objects at different places and also at different times of day at each place. Pick different latitudes of the two places so that the difference in latitude compensates for the difference in time of day and the sun's rays are thus at the same angle.

Explore More

The drawing at right demonstrates the construction. Reflect the point D at the top of the flagpole across the line representing the ground to create D'. Then connect the point representing the person's eye to D'. The point where this dashed line intersects the ground is the proper position of the mirror. (This construction actually follows the procedure incorrectly; in reality, you position the mirror first and then position your eye so that you can see the top of the flagpole in the mirror. A correct construction would be more complicated.)

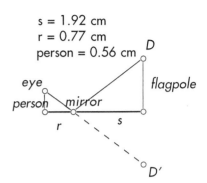

s = 1.92 cm
r = 0.77 cm
person = 0.56 cm

Lesson 12.5

Corresponding Parts of Similar Triangles

Example Sketches

• Similar Δ Parts (Mac) or ch12\simtript.gsp (Windows)

Discovering Geometry Correlation/Lesson Guide

This activity replaces Lesson 12.5 in *Discovering Geometry*. Consider splitting Investigate questions 1, 2, and 3 among different groups.

Construction Tips: Investigation 12.5.1

You can save time by having students start with the prepared sketch, Similar Triangles (Mac) or simtris.gsp (Windows). If they do, they can skip steps 1–7.

Investigate

1. Altitudes in similar triangles are proportional to corresponding sides.

2. Medians in similar triangles are proportional to corresponding sides.

3. Angle bisectors in similar triangles are proportional to corresponding sides.

4. If two triangles are similar, then the corresponding altitudes, corresponding medians, and corresponding angle bisectors are proportional to the corresponding sides (C-105: Proportional Parts Conjecture).

5. The angle bisector in a triangle divides the opposite side into two segments whose lengths are in the same ratio as the lengths of the two sides forming the angle (C-106).

Lesson 12.6

Proportion with Area and Volume

Example Sketches

• Proportion w/Area (Mac) or ch12\proparea.gsp (Windows)

Discovering Geometry Correlation/Lesson Guide

Investigation 12.6.1 from *Discovering Geometry* explores the relationship between the areas of similar figures. This lesson covers this concept quite thoroughly, and even extends the comparison of the areas of similar figures by demonstrating the relationship on the *x-y* plane.

Investigation 12.6.2 in *Discovering Geometry* addresses the subsequent conjecture about volumes of similar solids. This activity addresses this concept in Explore More 1. If you are concerned about covering all the material from Lesson 12.6 in a single day, make sure that students get to the Explore More, or have them read Investigation 12.6.2 as part of their homework.

Construction Tips: Investigation 12.6.1

Step 3: To construct a polygon interior, select a polygon's vertices in order, then use the Construct menu.

Step 4: To mark a point as a center double-click it with the selection arrow.

Step 5: Dilate means the same thing as scale. When you dilate objects, you shrink or stretch them toward or away from a center of dilation by some scale factor.

Steps 6–8: Make sure students compare the dilated figure to the original figure every time. If they reverse the order, the calculations will be misleading. The dilated figure's labels should be identified by the ´ symbol.

Step 8: You might want to have students record their predictions for the area ratios more formally, but its fine for them just to jot them down anywhere.

Step 10: Students should get a parabolic trace like the one in the figure.

Investigate

1. Ratios of Side Lengths and Ratios of Areas in Similar Figures

Ratio of side lengths	2	3	1	1/2	1/10	a/b
Ratio of areas	4	9	1	0.25 or 1/4	0.01 or 1/100	a^2/b^2

2. If two similar polygons (or circles) have the corresponding sides (or radii) in the ratio of m/n, then their areas are in the ratio of m^2/n^2 (C-107: Proportional Area Conjecture).

3. Students may recognize the graph traced by the plotted point as that of half a parabola, implying that the side-length ratio is proportional to the square of the area ratio. If the ratios were directly related, the graph would have been a straight line.

Explore More

1. a. If you have cubes handy, its best to have students construct these as well as sketch them. A simple example is to compare a cube of side length 1 with a cube of side length 2. Their respective volumes are 1 and 8. So a side length ratio of 1/2 results in a volume ratio of 1/8.

   b. If two similar solids have corresponding dimensions in the ratio of m/n, then their volumes are in the ratio of m^2/n^2 (C-108: Proportional Volume Conjecture).

The relevance of this concept can be brought home by asking students, "Why do you think the largest land animals, such as elephants and even dinosaurs, are so much smaller than the largest sea animals?" A land animal's weight must be supported by means of its skeleton. For a land animal to become twice as big, its volume—and hence its weight—would become eight times as large. But the strength of the bones would only increase by a factor of 4, since bone strength is proportional to the cross-sectional area of the bone. As a result, the larger animal's strength-to-weight ratio would only be half what it was before, and it would have difficulty supporting its own weight.

Lesson 12.7

Proportional Segments by Parallel Lines

Example Sketches

• Proportional Segments (Mac) or ch12\propsegs.gsp (Windows)

Discovering Geometry Correlation/Lesson Guide

This activity replaces Lesson 12.7 in *Discovering Geometry*. Investigations 12.7.1 and 12.7.2 are combined here.

Construction Tips: Investigations 12.7.1 and 12.7.2

Steps 6 and 7: Selection order is important when measuring ratios. Reversing selection order will measure reciprocal ratios.

Investigate

1. The ratios of corresponding segments are equal.

2. $\overline{DE}$ is parallel to $\overline{AC}$.

3. Note: This conjecture is worded slightly differently from the wording in the text because students in this activity divided two sides of a triangle with a segment instead of with a line. If a segment parallel to one side of a triangle has endpoints on the other two sides, then it divides them proportionally. Conversely, if a segment cuts two sides of a triangle proportionally, then it is parallel to the third side (C-109: Parallel Proportionality Conjecture).

Construction Tips: Investigation 12.7.3

Step 3: In this step you construct two lines parallel to a side of the triangle. Each line passes through the third side.

Investigate

4. If two or more lines pass through two sides of a triangle parallel to the third side, then they divide the two sides proportionally (C-10: Extended Parallel Proportionality Conjecture).

Explore More

By extending the sides of each triangle, you can show that angles are congruent because they're corresponding angles formed by parallel lines and transversals. Therefore, the triangles are similar by the AA Similarity Conjecture.

Lesson 13.1

Trigonometric Ratios

Example Sketches

Trig Ratios (Mac) or ch13\trig.gsp (Windows)

Discovering Geometry Correlation/Lesson Guide

This activity replaces Lesson 13.1 in *Discovering Geometry*. Students learn the definitions of tangent, sine, and cosine, and discover relationships and patterns among these ratios. The questions go beyond what students discover in the text lesson, but if you do this activity, make sure students see examples of how to use trigonometric ratios to solve problems like the example problems in the text. You should also make sure students know how to use their calculators. You might want to take two days to do this activity and the lesson in the text.

Construction Tips

Steps 1–5: A right triangle constructed this way will be easy to scale without changing its angles. Make sure students use this method and not some other method for constructing a right triangle.

Step 6: The Text tool turns black when the finger is positioned over an object. The letter A appears when the finger is positioned over a label.

Investigate

1. When the angles change, the ratios change.

2. When the angles don't change, the triangle stays similar to what it was before it was dragged. So side lengths stay in the same ratio.

3. $\sin A = m/l;\ \cos A = j/l$

4. $\tan 30° \approx 0.577;\ \sin 30° \approx 0.5;\ \cos 30° \approx 0.866$

5. Students should find that $\tan(m\angle CAB) = m/j$, $\sin(m\angle CAB) = m/l$, and $\cos(m\angle CAB) = j/l$.

6. As long as $m\angle A = 30°$, $m\angle B = 60°$. For acute angles A and B in right $\triangle ABC$, $\sin B = \cos A$ because the side opposite $\angle B$ is the side adjacent to $\angle A$, and vice versa.

7. a. $\angle C$ is a right angle, and the triangle can have only one right angle. As $\angle A$ approaches a right angle, point B moves far away.

    b. The value of $\tan 90°$ is undefined because the length of the adjacent side approaches 0. Students may say "infinity" because the tangent grows without bound as the angle approaches 90°. But make sure students realize that the tangent ratio is approaching a division by 0 and that they should use the term *undefined*.

    c. $\sin 90° = 1$

    d. $\sin 0° = 0$

    e. $\tan 45° = 1$. A right triangle with a 45° angle is isosceles. Therefore, opposite/adjacent = 1.

    f. $\sin 45° = \cos 45°$ because opposite = adjacent, and hence opposite/hypotenuse = adjacent/hypotenuse.

    g. $\sin x = \cos(90° - x)$

Lesson 13.3

The Law of Sines

Example Sketches

Law of Sines (Mac) or ch13\lawsine.gsp (Windows)

Discovering Geometry Correlation/Lesson Guide

This activity replaces Lesson 13.3 in *Discovering Geometry*. The investigations in that lesson depend primarily on students deriving the law of sines through pencil-and-paper work, as do the investigations here. The advantage to students deriving the law of sines with Sketchpad is that students can confirm that the expressions they derive actually work.

Construction Tips

Step 4: Choose sin[in the Functions menu of the calculator, click on $m\angle BAC$ in the sketch, then click the close parenthesis on the calculator.

Investigate

1. $A = (1/2)bh$

2. Since $\sin C = h/a$, $h = a \sin C$.

3. The area of a triangle is given by the formula $A = (1/2)ab \sin C$, where a and b are the lengths of two sides and C is the acute angle between them (C-111).

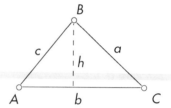

4. The three expressions all give the area of the same triangle, using a different vertex from which to measure the height. Thus they must equal each other.

5. $\sin A/a = \sin B/b = \sin C/c$

Project
Non-Euclidean Geometries

Required Sketch/Scripts

Poincaré Disk Starter (Mac sketch) or Poincar\Poincare.gsp (Windows sketch)

all scripts in the Poincare folder

Discovering Geometry Correlation/Lesson Guide

This project correlates closely with the second half of Project: Non-Euclidean Geometries that follows Lesson 15.1 in *Discovering Geometry*. The Poincaré disk is the model of hyperbolic geometry described in that project. You can do this project sometime near the beginning of a whole unit on non-Euclidean geometry. Students can start with geometry on a sphere (elliptic geometry) and compare it with Euclidean geometry and then with geometry on the Poincaré disk. (On a sphere, there are no parallel lines. On the disk, there are many lines parallel to a given line through a given point. On a sphere, the sum of the angle measures in a triangle is greater than 180°. On the disk, the sum is less than 180°.)

Using the Poincaré script tools, students can carry out many interesting constructions and investigations of their own choosing.

Investigate

1. This worksheet is intentionally devoid of pictures so that students will see for themselves (and be surprised by) how the tools behave. They should make some of the following observations:

    • Lines are arcs of circles that end at the edge of the disk. They meet the disk at right angles.

    • Circles are like Euclidean circles except that their centers are skewed toward the edge of the disk.

    • The closer a line or a segment comes to passing through the center of the disk, the straighter it is.

    • Distances increase faster as you move toward the edge of the disk.

    • If two segments have a common endpoint near the edge of the disk, the measure of the angle they form is close to 0. (Students aren't likely to notice it, but angle measures are defined by the tangents to the arcs where two Poincaré segments or lines meet to form an angle.)

2. The line meets the edge of the disk at right angles.

3. Infinitely many lines can be drawn that don't intersect the given line. Poincaré geometry is based on Assumption 1: Through a given point not on a given line there pass more than one line parallel to the given line.

4. Radii that go toward the center of the disk appear longer than radii that go toward the edge. Distances near the edge of the disk get compressed.

5. The sum of the angle measures in a triangle on the Poincaré disk is between 0° and 180°.

6. The base angles of an isosceles triangle are congruent.

7. Encourage students to try constructions and investigations of their own using some of the tools in the Other folder.

Lesson 16.7
Midsegment Conjectures

Example Sketches

• Quadrilateral Midsegments (Mac) or ch15_16\quadmdsg.gsp (Windows)

Discovering Geometry Correlation/Lesson Guide

This activity replaces Lesson 16.7 in *Discovering Geometry*. The investigation is ideal for Sketchpad because the construction is easy and the result is surprising. The insight gained by drawing a diagonal is also more striking in a dynamic sketch. Students can probably write paragraph proofs of these conjectures. If you want flow-chart proofs, you should go over the proof on page 774 with the class. But save it until after students discover the conjecture. It's worth answering the Explore More questions. These results are perhaps even more surprising than the midpoint quadrilateral. The constructions can be tricky, however.

Investigation: An Arbitrary Quadrilateral

Investigate

1. The midpoint quadrilateral is a parallelogram. Opposite sides are congruent.

2. a. $\overline{GF}$ is parallel to $\overline{BD}$ and half as long.

   b. $\overline{HE}$ is also parallel to $\overline{BD}$ and half as long.

   c. $\overline{GF}$ is parallel and congruent to $\overline{HE}$. (This is enough to conclude that *GFEH* is a parallelogram.)

   d. Segments *HG* and *EF* are both midsegments of triangles with base *AC*, so they're parallel and congruent to each other.

3. Segments $\overline{GF}$ and *HE* are midsegments of triangles with base *BD*. By the Triangle Midsegment Theorem (T-50) $\overline{GF}$ is parallel to $\overline{BD}$ and $\overline{HE}$ is parallel to $\overline{BD}$. Therefore, *GF* is parallel to *HE*. Similarly, segments *HG* and *EF* are both midsegments of triangles with base *AC*, so they're parallel to each other.

Investigation: Special Quadrilaterals

The midpoint quadrilateral of a rectangle is a rhombus. Proof: The diagonals of a rectangle are congruent. Therefore, the midsegments of the triangles formed by drawing diagonals in a rectangle are congruent.

The midpoint quadrilateral of a rhombus is a rectangle. Proof: The diagonals of a rhombus are perpendicular. Therefore, the midsegments of the triangles formed by drawing one diagonal of the rhombus are perpendicular to the midsegments of the triangles formed by drawing the other diagonal.

The midpoint quadrilateral of an isosceles trapezoid is a rhombus. Proof: The diagonals of an isosceles trapezoid are congruent. Therefore, the midsegments of the triangles formed by drawing diagonals in an isosceles triangle are congruent.

The midpoint quadrilateral of a square is a square. Proof: Because the diagonals of a square are perpendicular, the midsegments of the triangles formed by drawing one diagonal are perpendicular to the midsegments of the triangles formed by drawing the other diagonal. Because the diagonals of a square are congruent, the midsegments of the triangles formed by drawing the diagonals are also congruent.

The midpoint quadrilateral of a kite is a rectangle. Proof: The diagonals of a kite are perpendicular. Therefore, the midsegments of the triangles formed by drawing one diagonal of the kite are perpendicular to the midsegments of the triangles formed by drawing the other diagonal.

Explore More

1. Rhombuses and kites have rectangles for midpoint quadrilaterals. Rhombuses and kites both have perpendicular diagonals. Any quadrilateral with perpendicular diagonals has a rectangle for its midpoint quadrilateral.

2. Rectangles and isosceles trapezoids have rhombuses for midpoint quadrilaterals. Rectangles and isosceles trapezoids both have congruent diagonals. Any quadrilateral with congruent diagonals has a rhombus for its midpoint quadrilateral.

3. A square has a square for its midpoint quadrilateral. The diagonals of a square are both congruent and perpendicular. Any quadrilateral whose diagonals are congruent and perpendicular has a square for its midpoint quadrilateral.

To construct the most general possible quadrilaterals that have special midpoint quadrilaterals, you can take one of two approaches. The first approach is to start by constructing a pair of diagonals with the necessary characteristics. For example, to construct a quadrilateral whose midpoint quadrilateral is a rectangle, construct a pair of perpendicular segments, then draw the quadrilateral that has these segments for diagonals. The example sketch Special Midpoint Quads (Mac) or ch16\mdptqua2.gsp (Windows) uses this approach.

A second approach is to start by constructing the midpoint quadrilateral, then use the Line tool and the Circle tool to draw a quadrilateral around it that has the vertices of the midpoint quadrilateral for midpoints. An example of such a construction is shown at right. In this example, rectangle *ABDC* was constructed first, then line *AE*, circle *AE*, line *FB*, circle *BF*, line *GD*, circle *DG*, and, finally, line *HC*, which passes through point *E*.

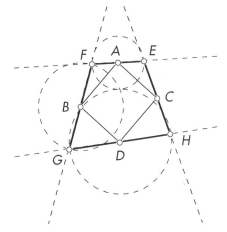

Lesson 0.2
Line Designs

Example Sketches

• Line Design (Mac) or ch02\linedes.gsp (Windows)

Discovering Geometry Correlation/Lesson Guide

In Lesson 0.2 in *Discovering Geometry,* students see more than just this type of line design, and they get practice using a straightedge to make careful drawings. You might want the class to do the lesson in the book and save this activity for an extension later in the year.

Construction Tips

Step 11: To avoid errant segments, have students select the two points they want to connect and then choose Segment in the Construct menu.

Step 12: Highlight the Point tool and choose Select All Points in the Edit menu. Holding down Shift, click on points *A, B,* and *C* to deselect them before you choose Hide Points in the Display menu.

Step 14: Highlight the Segment tool and choose Select All Segments in the Edit menu.

Investigate

1. The line through points *A* and *B* is the only line of symmetry.

2. a. The figure below left has two lines of symmetry: through points *A* and *B* and through points *A* and *C.*

   b. The figure below center has four lines of symmetry: one through points *A* and *B,* one through points *A* and *C,* and two more at 45° angles to those.

   c. The figure below right has three lines of symmetry: one through each corner, passing through the center. (This figure is hard to make. Two sets of segments overlap to reduce the four sets to three.)

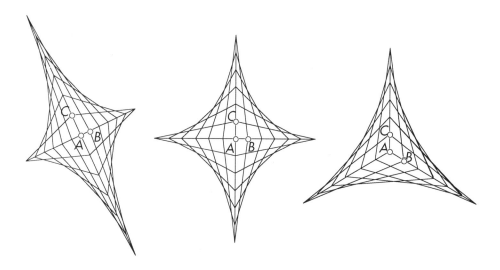

Explore More

Students can try dynamic versions of the examples in Lesson 0.2 of *Discovering Geometry.*

Lesson 0.3

Daisy Designs

Example Sketches

• Hex Designs (Mac sketch) or ch00\hexdes.gsp (Windows sketch)

Discovering Geometry Correlation/Lesson Guide

In Lesson 0.3 in *Discovering Geometry,* students get practice using a compass, so don't replace that lesson with this one. Instead, use this lesson as an extension or save it for later in the year.

Construction Tips

Step 2: Make sure students use points *B* and *A* to define the second circle. Some may use *B* for the center of a circle that merely passes through *A* but whose radius is defined by a third point. That will cause their designs to fall apart if dragged.

Step 5: Sketchpad will not allow the construction of an intersection of three objects, as such an intersection is not usually defined by a single point. To construct an intersection of three objects, you must select two of them and use the Construct menu.

Step 6: Point out that by using the Segment tool to connect the outside points of the daisy students can construct a regular hexagon. They can construct a six-pointed star by connecting alternate points to create intersecting equilateral triangles. Midpoints can be useful in creating more complex designs. Encourage students to experiment and practice using different tools.

Lesson 0.4

Op Art

Example Sketches and Scripts

- Tumbling Blocks (Mac sketch) or ch00\tumblk.gsp (Windows sketch)
- 6/Hexagon (Inscribed) (Mac script) or regpoly\6inscrib.gss (Windows)

Discovering Geometry Correlation/Lesson Guide

This lesson can replace Lesson 0.4 in *Discovering Geometry,* though some familiarity with Sketchpad would be very useful. Don't make this your introduction to Sketchpad. You could make this activity an optional approach for students who show particular interest in working on computers, or save it for later in the school year.

Construction Tips

Step 3: Construct the intersection of any two diagonals.

Step 4: The segments and polygon interiors constructed in this step divide the hexagon into three congruent rhombuses.

Step 5: Student labels are unlikely to match the figure. Students need to select appropriate points to translate the figure horizontally by the width of the block.

Step 6: Select All is in the Edit menu when the Selection Arrow tool is chosen in the Toolbox. Make sure By Marked Vector is the checked choice in the Translate dialog.

Step 7: As long as you don't click anywhere, the translated figure from the previous step will be selected, ready to translate again.

Step 12: Choose the Point tool and choose Select All Points in the Edit menu. While all the points are selected, hold down Shift, choose the Selection Arrow tool, and click on *A* and *B* to deselect them. Hide the remaining selected points.

Investigate

1. If they're familiar with the terms *hexagon* and *rhombus*, students should note that the tumbling block design is comprised of regular hexagons divided into rhombuses. Point out to students that this is an example of a tessellation, or a tiling of the plane without gaps or overlap.

2. The blocks tend to pop in and out. One moment you see blocks coming out of the page, and another moment it may appear as if you're looking up from beneath and new blocks appear, with the old blocks turning inside out.

Lesson 0.7

Islamic Art

Example Sketches and Scripts

- Islamic Art (Mac sketch) or ch00\Islamic.gsp (Windows sketch)
- 4/Square (Inscribed) (Mac script) or regpoly\4inscrib.gss (Windows script)

Discovering Geometry Correlation/Lesson Guide

This lesson can replace Lesson 0.7 in *Discovering Geometry,* though some familiarity with Sketchpad would be very useful. Don't make this your introduction to Sketchpad. You could make this activity an optional approach for students who show particular interest in working on computers, or save it for later in the school year.

Construction Tips

Step 1: Students need not use a script to construct a square, but one way or another they need to start with a square. The square script is available in the Sample Sketches folder that comes with Sketchpad as well as in the Chapter 00 folder on the disk that accompanies this book.

Step 5: Click at the intersection with the Point tool or the Selection Arrow tool.

Step 8: Students may have other ways to draw the knot design that they find easier than the one described here. If they have trouble following step 9, encourage them to try their own methods.

Step 11: To construct a polygon interior, select the points at the vertices of the region and choose Polygon Interior in the Construct menu. With a hint, some students might note that they need only construct two polygon interiors of contrasting colors, which can then be rotated 90° to color the rest of the knot.

Step 15: The easiest way to hide a lot of points is to highlight the Point tool, choose Select All Points in the Edit menu, hold down Shift and click on the points you don't want to hide to deselect them, and then choose Hide Points in the Display menu.

Explore More

Refer students to Example B on page 24 of *Discovering Geometry* for an example of a hexagon-based design.

Lesson 0.8

Perspective

Example Sketches

- 2-Pt. Perspective Box or ch00\perspect.gsp
- Cabin (Mac) or ch00\cabin.gsp (Windows)

Discovering Geometry Correlation/Lesson Guide

Use this lesson in place of, or as an extension to, Lesson 0.8 in *Discovering Geometry*. Of all the Chapter 0 Sketchpad activities, this is the most accessible to Sketchpad novices. Students enjoy doing perspective drawing, and this lesson could serve as a motivating introduction to Sketchpad.

Construction Tips

Follow the steps in the activity carefully and sequentially to ensure that your box obeys the rules of two-point perspective when you move it.

Steps 1–2: Hold down Shift while drawing the horizon line and front edge to make it easy to make horizontal and vertical segments.

Step 9: Students could stop at this step if they're content with bottomless boxes. Students should drag their front edge above the horizon line just to see that their box has no bottom.

Investigate

For space reasons, this activity sheet has no Investigate section. However, you can ask students to write descriptions of what happens as they move the horizon line or vanishing points. How can they look at the bottom of the box? What's the position of the viewer when the horizon line is above the box? What effect does moving the vanishing points farther apart have on the view of the box?

Explore More

(Not on student worksheet.) Students can create all kinds of more complicated drawings of houses, office buildings, or whole city blocks using two-point perspective. You can have students try boxes with one-point perspective (viewing a front face instead of a front edge). See the example sketch Cabin (Mac) or ch00\cabin.gsp (Windows).

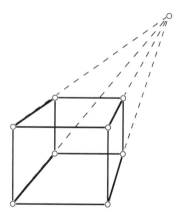

A box with one-point perspective